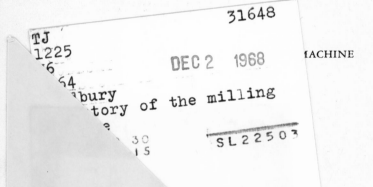

Robert S. Woodbury

HISTORY OF THE MILLING MACHINE

A Study in Technical Development

THE M.I.T. PRESS
Massachusetts Institute of Technology
Cambridge, Massachusetts

For
JOSEPH WICKHAM ROE
who first showed
the importance of
machine tools
in history

The publication of this study is made possible by the interest and generosity of the Wilkie Foundation and the DoALL Company, Des Plaines, Illinois.

TABLE OF CONTENTS

PREFACE

The aim in the present monograph on the History of the Milling Machine is not only to survey the history of this most significant tool, but also to use it as an example of the problems and historical methods involved in making a detailed analysis of the progress of the *technical* features of any piece of machinery. Such an analysis is an essential prerequisite to further and broader studies, for otherwise, important omissions or significant misinterpretations may easily creep into the work of even the most careful economic or social historian. Although the technical development of any machine tool is certainly influenced by the use to which it is put in production and by other characteristics of the economy of the time, there are for a given machine tool certain inherent capabilities and limitations which can only be resolved by the technical genius, no matter how great the other pressures for a solution.

Therefore, no attempt has been made here to do more than suggest the historical influence of the milling machine upon production and upon the economy. This is not to imply that there were no such effects, or even that they were of minor importance, for from the first the milling machine played a very significant part in the early manufacture of small arms by the principle of interchangeable parts[1], and from this beginning its use spread into every industry using machine tools.

This monograph, although the third to be published, was actually the first of the series to be written. Because its publication by the Smithsonian Institution was expected in 1958, it is so referred to in my *History of the Gear Cutting Machine.*

1. This development will be discussed in more detail in my monograph *History of Shop Precision of Measurement and Interchangeable Parts.*

9

My indebtedness for scholarly assistance is indicated at the relevant points in the text. Mr. A. William Meyer, of Brown & Sharpe, gave me generous access to source material in their files, as did Mr. Sam Redrow, Jr. and Mr. Mario Martellotti of the Cincinnati Milling Machine Company.

ROBERT S. WOODBURY

Cambridge, Massachusetts
February 1, 1959

INTRODUCTION

One hundred years ago a machine shop considered itself well equipped if it had a good screw-cutting lathe with back gears, a chain drive planer, and an adequate drill press.[1] Only a few specialized shops could boast any kind of a milling machine. Today even the smallest of shops find some sort of milling machine a necessity; and the lathe, which has been the basic machine tool from the beginning, now finds itself seriously challenged by the versatility and convenience of the milling machine. This most useful machine has now developed into fully automatic types, the vertical spindle form, and the tracing die-sinker, to the point where it performs many metal-cutting operations not possible by any means a century earlier.

This progress has been the result of invention and technological advance of prime importance to the whole growth of our industrial society. Almost the entire development of the milling machine took place in the United States, in fact in a few centers — at first principally in New England and later also in the Mid-West. These machines were rather rapidly adopted by manufacturers of small arms, sewing machines, etc., in the U.S.A.[2] British manufacturers were generally slow to adopt milling methods of metalworking,

1. James Fletcher, "On Improvement in Heavy Tools," *Pro. Inst. Mech. Eng.*, 1864, p. 189.
2. For the users of the Lincoln type miller, see sales records of Pratt & Whitney Co., Hartford, Conn., who manufactured thousands of this type. For the universal milling machine, see sales records of Brown & Sharpe Manufacturing Co., Providence, R.I., and Luther D. Burlingame, in *American Machinist*, 1911, pp. 9-13.

in fact not until 1890-1910.[3] However, by the period 1870-1880 continental manufacturers were already utilizing these machines, at first largely of American makers,[4] but by 1873 they were also using inferior continental copies of American designs.[5] This situation continued until as late as 1908.[6]

In order to avoid some confusion that has arisen in the past about the history of the milling machine, it seems wise to define our terms. In this study the milling machine will be taken to be basically: a *generalized* machine tool in which metal is removed by a rotary multiple-tooth cutter from a workpiece secured to a table whose motion relative to the cutter is controlled in any combination of longitudinal, transverse, or vertical feeds. This definition relegates to other monographs the gear-cutting and other horological tools of Robert Hooke of about 1672,[7] and the interesting tools of the French and English clockmakers of the mid-18th century, such as Fardoil and Thiout,[8] Hindley, Rehé, and

3. Apparently because British manufacturers put their few imported machines to doing far heavier work than either the cutters or the machines were designed for. See George Addy, "On Milling Cutters," *Pro. Inst. Mech. Eng.*, 1890, p. 528. Compare the quite different attitudes expressed in John J. Grant, "The Milling Machine as a Substitute for the Planer in Machine Construction," *Trans. Am. Soc. Mech. Eng.*, Vol. 9, 1887-1888, pp. 259-269, but also note the machine used for very heavy work described p. 104 of *Practical Mechanics Journal*, Vol. I, Glasgow, 1848.

4. Cf. Brown & Sharpe sales records. Also Luther D. Burlingame, in *American Machinist*, 1911, p. 9.

5. In some cases the copies still had the names of the original manufacturers reproduced on the machine! (Robert H. Thurston, *Report on Machinery and Manufacturers, Vienna International Exhibition 1873*, Washington, GPO, 1875, p. 202.) British manufacturers also indulged in this practice. (Thomas R. Pickering, "American Machinery at International Exhibitions," *Trans. Am. Soc. Mech. Eng.*, Vol. V, 1883, pp. 113-121.)

6. Godfrey L. Carden, *Machine Tool Trade in Germany, France, Switzerland, Italy and United Kingdom*, Washington, GPO, 1909, passim.

7. H. Robinson and W. Adams, eds., *Diary of Robert Hooke 1672-1680*, London, 1935, entries of 16 August 1672, 18 and 20 March 1672/73, 2 May, 27 June, and 7 October 1674. References to dates of 1664 and 1675 are merely indications of the general lack of scholarly care in writing on the history of tools and of horology.

8. Antoine Thiout, *Traité de l'horlogerie méchanique et practique*, Paris, 1741. Ferdinand Berthoud, *Essai sur l'horlogerie*, 3 vols., Paris, 1763 and 1786. Diderot's *Encyclopédie*, Paris, 1772, Article "Horlogerie."

Ramsden,[9] as well as Bramah's very interesting wood "planing machine" of 1802,[10] and Villon's machines of 1716 for
ordnance.[11]

9. R. S. Woodbury, *History of the Gear-Cutting Machine*, The Technology
Press, 1958.

10. Abraham Rees, *Cyclopedia or Universal Dictionary of Arts, Sciences
and Literature*, Philadelphia, first American edition, 1805-1825, Article
"Planing Machines." Joseph W. Roe, *English and American Tool Builders*,
New York, 1926, says (p. 18) "He used this same method in planing the
metal parts for his locks, which corresponds, of course, to our modern face
milling." Roe's source is not given, but is probably Samuel Smiles, *Industrial Biography*, Boston, 1864, p. 238. However, Smiles merely says "Although the machinery described in the patent was first applied to working
in wood, it was equally applicable to working in metals; and in his own
shops at Pimlico, Bramah employed a machine with revolving cuttters to
plane metallic surfaces for his patent locks and other articles." Smiles does
not give a source for this statement, nor does he tell us what type of machine
it was nor when it was first in use. The Science Museum, London, has in
its collections several cutters which may be Bramah's, but they cannot be
dated with certainty. (Sci. Mus. Inv. 1935-131.) In his *Dissertation on the
Construction of Locks*, London, ca. 1815, Bramah does not describe the
method of manufacture of the locks, only their design.

11. *Machines et inventions approuvées par l'Académie Royale des Sciences*,
Vol. 3, 1716-1719, Paris, 1735. Villon's machines are numbers 166 and 167.

I The Pioneers

ELI WHITNEY

ROBERT JOHNSON

JAMES NASMYTH

THE PIONEERS

The first milling machines of which we have any clear records at all are those of Eli Whitney, Robert Johnson, and James Nasmyth. Of these Whitney and Johnson probably influenced each other, are clearly the earliest, and we have what may be an actual Whitney machine. Nasmyth's is probably an independent invention, is clearly later than the other two, and is better documented. In all three the exact nature of their cutters remains unclear, and perhaps all should more correctly be labeled rotary filing machines. Nasmyth so referred to his.

FIG. 1. ELI WHITNEY'S MILLING MACHINE OF ABOUT 1820.
The oldest existing milling machine.
(*New Haven Colony Historical Society*)

Eli Whitney

The early Whitney milling machine [1] (Fig. 1) rediscovered in 1912 through the efforts of Joseph W. Roe was identified by Eli Whitney's grandson of the same name as having been pointed out to him since boyhood as built by Eli Whitney and as the first miller ever built. Roe seems to have dated it as of 1818 merely from the statement in the Encyclopedia Britannica that "the first very crude milling machine was made in 1818 in a gun factory in Connecticut" and assuming that this could refer to no other than the Whitneyville plant.[2] The sources for the statement in the Encyclopedia Britannica are unknown, but at least we know that in 1818 North's and Johnson's gun factories, among others, were operating in Middletown, Connecticut, and we have equally good evidence that a milling machine not too different from Whitney's was in use there. The first clear evidence we have of Whitney's use of milling is contained in his letter of 20 March 1823 to John C. Calhoun, then Secretary of War. By that date milling was already in use in the Armories at both Springfield and Harper's Ferry.[3] However, from the evidence and its design features it is the oldest milling machine extant, as well as the most significant in its influence on later machines.

Roe's original description of this machine is masterly:

"It stands about 18 inches high and is about 2 feet 6 inches square over-all. The base is a solid wooden block

1. Now in the collection of the New Haven Colony Historical Society, New Haven, Connecticut, having been partially restored after part of the feed mechanism was lost while on loan to the now defunct Museum of the Peaceful Arts in New York.

2. Joseph W. Roe, "History of the First Milling Machine," *American Machinist*, 1912, pp. 1037-38. *Encyclopaedia Britannica*, 11th edition, article "Tools."

3. See below p. 20 for Johnson. For the Armories see below p. 30. For North see the documents reprinted in James E. Hicks, *United States Ordnance*, Mt. Vernon, New York, 1940, Vol. II, Chap. VII, "Simon North, 1800-1841." North may have used a milling machine as early as 1808. The author has checked all pertinent documents in Hicks with the originals in the U. S. National Archives and in the Sterling Library, Yale University.

carried on short, light, wrought iron legs. The main spindle, about 2½ inches in diameter, was driven by a single pulley, which must have been about 20 inches in diameter, as the wooden base was gouged out a little to clear it.[4] The spindle ran in solid soft-metal bearings in two flat housings, bolted to the square box-like frame.

"The connection between these uprights and the frame is so rough that it does not seem, even allowing for 90 years of rust, to have ever been a machine fit.[5] On the inner end of the rear bearing [6] is a wrought iron plate, which engages in a groove on the spindle which controlled its position lengthwise.[7]

". . . The slide, jam and gib-bolts are lost. The slide ran between a gibbed bracket, cast on the frame, and one of the V's on the front bearing support.

"The feed was taken from the double grooved wooden pulley between the spindle bearings down to the lower shaft by a round belt, the return side of which ran up through a hole in the wooden base, . . . A wooden cam, two wrought iron plates and a swinging bearing carried the rear end of the worm shaft, the front end of which could be raised and lowered.

"The short bearing between the handle and the worm was carried on a small, vertical slide, which has a spring latch to hold it in the engaged position. By dropping the latch, the worm on the feed shaft was disengaged to allow hand feeding.

4. A fact overlooked in the otherwise splendid working model reconstruction of this machine made in the early 1930's by Mr. "Wint" Trible for Mr. Frederick V. Geier, President, Cincinnati Milling Machine Co. and still in their possession. Also not noted in the equally fine reconstruction made for the Wilkie Foundation's outstanding exhibit "Civilization through Tools" now in the Chicago Museum of Science and Industry.

5. As long as the "connection" remained rigid, and provided the spindle bearings were properly fitted, this would not affect the accuracy of the machine.

6. Actually it is on the rear upright, not the bearing.

7. This provided a lengthwise adjustment of about ½ inch for the spindle. It is in no sense a cross feed, merely a means of adjusting the tool along the axis of the spindle after the work had been secured to the table.

"The feed screw was fairly well cut with what was originally a square thread, but along the middle, under the cutter, it has been worn to a sharp V. The keyways are rough-chipped, and some, at least, of the bolts appear to have been hand made.

". . . A glance at the worm wheel . . . shows that it was made before the days of involute teeth. It is made of wrought iron [8] and the worm is brass . . . It is a quaint little mechanism, but the smile it provokes usually dies away in very genuine respect." [9]

The respect of which Roe speaks should increase in the reader's mind as we see what a great influence this type of machine had on its successors and how long many of its features were retained. For example, even one hundred years later milling machines were common in industry which had very similar means of engaging the table power feed. It should also be noted that the Whitney machine had power feed for the table based on the use of nut-and-screw principle rather than the rack-and-pinion method that was to plague milling machine design for the next two generations. Later, devices to eliminate backlash, and improvements in precision cutting of gears, brought the rack-and-pinion drive back into very satisfactory use.

Whitney also incorporated in his base the box principle so essential to rigidity in later milling machines. And he has already included the use of gibs for holding down the table and taking up wear.

No provision was made on this machine for vertical adjustment of the tool relative to the table. However, it should be noted that this is the beginning of the column and knee type (as contrasted with the Lincoln type). It was soon followed in Bodmer's 1839 gear-cutting machine and later in Joseph R. Brown's universal milling machine and in many subsequent milling machines.

8. It is now only simulated in wood to replace the original part lost while on loan.
9. Joseph W. Roe, "History of the First Milling Machine," *American Machinist,* 1912, pp. 1037-38.

Robert Johnson

The hand milling machine shown in Fig. 2 is a reconstruction made in 1900 by E. G. Parkhurst [10] from his memory of the machine as he saw it in late 1851 and from something of its history from the lips of Robert Johnson, who said that it was the first he had ever known and was definitely first put to work in 1818 in a small arms factory which he and some other English gunmakers established in 1814 in Middletown, Connecticut.[11]

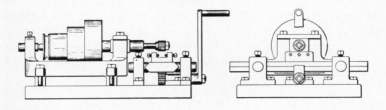

FIG. 2. THE MIDDLETOWN MILLING MACHINE OF 1818.
(*American Machinist*)

Parkhurst describes the machine as:

"Bolted to a wooden bench by four bolts was a base or bed-plate of rough cast iron about 18 x 24 inches, two inches thick. There was a head which had been removed from an engine lathe. Fitted to this was a spindle with a square taper socket, having one journal box and a rear step bearing. There were wood cone pulleys about 2½ inches face, and the largest about 8 inches in diameter; the grooved pulley for feed was added later. On the bed, at about 12 x 6¾ inches center distances, were bolted, with two bolts each, four upright stands about 4 inches in hight [*sic*], and these

10. E. G. Parkhurst, "One of the Earliest Milling Machines," *American Machinist*, 1900, p. 25-217.

11. This may be the source used in the *Encyclopaedia Britannica* article referred to on p. 17 above. Johnson offered to make rifles for the United States as early as March 22, 1814. See documents reprinted in James E. Hicks, *United States Ordnance*, Mt. Vernon, New York, 1940, Vol. II, p. 118.

were bored near the top to receive four round plugs that were secured by set screws from the top of the stands. The plugs were about 1½ inches in diameter, and had cut in the inner ends V notches about 90 degrees angle, in which were supported the angle edged table, about 20 x 5 inches, 1½ inches thick. On the under side of the table was, fastened by screws, a cast iron (cast tooth) rack, about 1⅛ inches face and 6 inches long. The cast tooth pinion, about 1¾ inches in diameter, was made fast to a shaft which had on its outer edge [sic] that projected over the bed a hand crank (about 10 inch centers); the same secured by square eye and nut. A stand bolted to the bed with two bolts supported the pinion shaft at such hight [sic] as secured the proper mesh of pinion and rack.

"The fixture for holding parts to be milled was made in the form of a trough, and had pointed set screws at each side. There was no adjustment whatever in the machine other than that at the side of the table to compensate for wear. Strips of metal or paper were used to pack under a piece should a recut be required.

". . . I have endeavored to show its principle rather than the exact pattern. My regret is that the machine did not find a resting place in some museum, instead of being consigned to a furnace cupola." [12]

This is a clear enough sketch and description, perhaps too clear to be relied on, but lacking anything better, let us see what we can get out of it. First, since Johnson did not claim the invention as his own, we are free to speculate about its origin. The use of a lathe head as a central feature and Johnson's English origin suggest that it may be an outgrowth of vague references we have to Maudslay's use of a lathe spindle to turn a rotary cutter to cut gear teeth and to plane surfaces held in some sort of attachment on either the lathe bed or the slide rest. And although Nasmyth's miller is

12. This strikes a warm note in the heart of any historian of technology, who must also regret that Parkhurst does not tell us that he made a little sketch in 1851 or at least that he put down some notes of what he saw and Johnson said. Eighty-two years, even forty-eight years, is a long time to rely upon human memory.

clearly later, it too used a lathe head (see Fig. 5) and is said[13] to have been built by Maudslay, Nasmyth having invented only the dividing head. On the other hand, the very close proximity of Middletown to Whitneyville, even by the communications standards of the time, together with the fact that nearly all these small arms factories were working on very similar government contracts, would suggest possible exchange of ideas and experience through workmen and government inspectors *sub rosa,* even if not done openly under the rather secretive practices about technical matters common in that day as well as our own. That there was mutual influence of this Middletown machine and the Whitney machine we can be fairly certain. What the direction of the greater influence may have been is more difficult to evaluate. Clearly the Middletown machine is a very inferior piece of machine design compared to Whitney's and lacks a number of important features that Whitney included, such as power feed. It might logically seem to follow that Whitney's machine was an improved form of the original invention of Middletown. However, from what we know of Eli Whitney's keen originality in inventing the cotton gin in practically its perfected form, as well as his breadth of technical vision in applying the principles of interchangeable parts and specialization of labor, the reverse seems to be more probable — that the Middletown machine either is an independent invention on a level below Whitney's or is perhaps based on a combination of English ideas with the bits of information about a superior machine that will inevitably escape from even the tightest industrial or military security.

Yet Parkhurst does provide us with the only clear information we have about some features of the milling machine at this period, enough so that we can at least make an "educated guess" at reconstruction of some parts of the Whitney machine that are missing — especially the cutter itself and the method of holding and adjusting the work.

13. E. P. Terry, "The Origin of the Milling Machine," *American Machinist,* 1921, p. 496. And James Nasmyth, *Autobiography* (ed. Samuel Smiles), London, 1883, p. 150.

Parkhurst says:

". . . There was no evidence to show that the machine was ever used on curved or irregular cuts, as the cutter I saw in the machine was a plain one [see Fig. 2], about 1½ inches in diameter and 1 inch face; the teeth in this cutter were filed out. Mr. Johnson also stated that at first the workmen did not take to the machine — considering it an innovation on filing, though later they used it to save hand labor in taking a roughing cut that would leave a surface flat."

This would seem to indicate that the cutters on these pioneer milling machines were, like those of the French clockmakers, essentially power-driven rotary files. The cutter of Vaucanson of prior to 1782 [14] (Fig. 3), being formed, could not be filed out and was prob-ably chipped with great skill. But it, too, is essentially a rotary file. The milling machine cutter as we think of it today, with large coarse teeth and cutting a substantial chip, was not to appear for another generation.

FIG. 3. VAUCANSON'S MILLING CUTTER
OF ABOUT 1760.
(*Brown & Sharpe*)

The method of holding the work on the Middletown miller is of great interest, for this machine had no means of adjustment of the table relative to the cutter either trans-versely or vertically. The use of opposing pointed set screws would give about ½ inch transversely, about the same as Whitney's, but with much finer adjustment of the work possible, as well as greater convenience. The round vee table guides could be used to give transverse adjustment,

14. Luther D. Burlingame, "History of the Milling Machine," *Iron Trade Review*, 1915, p. 922 (a portion of a more extensive treatment in Burlin-game's MS. in the files of Brown & Sharpe Manufacturing Co., Providence, R. I.)

but this would require careful alignment (as would the pointed set-screws) to ensure that the desired cut runs perpendicular to the cutter spindle. These adjustments would not be required on the Whitney machine. The use of paper or metal shims to get vertical adjustment would also seem to have been the method used by Whitney, but since its table, together with any holding device, was lost long before Roe found it, we cannot be sure. At any rate it is a method still in common use in machine shops today.

James Nasmyth

Nasmyth's miller can fortunately be dated and described with much greater certainty than either the Whitney or the Middletown machine, since we know that it was built shortly after he entered the employ of Henry Maudslay in May 1829[15] and certainly prior to Maudslay's death in 1831.[16]

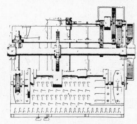

FIG. 4. WILLIS' HEAVY MILLING MACHINE OF 1845. (*Practical Mechanics Journal*)

Perhaps this machine is too specialized to be included under our definition of a milling machine, since Nasmyth designed it primarily for milling the sides of nuts.[17] But it does have a number of interesting features. There may be a connection between this canny Scotsman and the very heavy crank milling machine (Fig. 4) designed in 1845 by Robert Willis for the Railway Foundry, Leeds,[18] but the two designs are fundamentally different, and from the size and character of Willis' machine it would appear to be more a stepchild of Bramah's "planing machine" of 1802. We shall have reason to consider some features of Willis' machine later.

15. Nasmyth, *Autobiography*, p. 146.

16. Samuel Smiles, *Industrial Biography*, Boston, 1864, pp. 338-340.

17. However, the diagram at the upper right in Fig. 5 and the extra holes in the table suggest that it may have had a broader use later.

18. L. L. Thwing, "The Origin of the Milling Machine," *American Machinist*, 1921, p. 1085. John J. Grant, "The Milling Machine as a Substitute for the Planer," *Trans. Am. Soc. Mech. Eng.*, Vol. IX, 1887/1888, p. 267. *Practical Mechanic's Journal*, Vol. I, 1848, pp. 97 and 104.

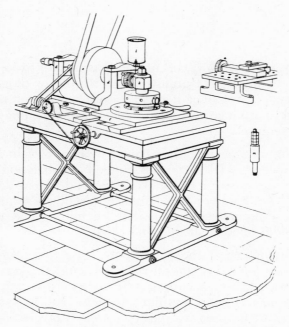

FIG. 5. NASMYTH'S MILLER OF ABOUT 1830.
(*Buchanan*)

Although Nasmyth was especially pleased with what he calls "this clever little tool," (Fig. 5)[19] hindsight indicates some defects — the feed was intermittent rather than continuous, although the dimensions would indicate that for the small collar-nuts it was intended to machine, this would have still produced a good finish. The power feed was of very light construction for the size of the cross slide, but probably adequate for the small collar-nuts, and it is a screw and nut type. One must admit that the power feed was

19. The illustration shown is from Nasmyth's own account published in Robertson Buchanan, *Practical Essays on Mill Work and Other Machinery*, London, 1841, Appendix B and Plate XXXIX. This differs somewhat from the drawing and description given in Nasmyth's *Autobiography*. It probably represents the form which Nasmyth, Gaskell and Company later manufactured, while the *Autobiography* drawing is likely the form which Nasmyth originally made for Maudslay. The Science Museum, London, has a model of a machine shop (Sci. Mus. Inv., 1927-1051) which has milling machines (Nos. 11 and 48) clearly later models of Nasmyth's. In Box 50 of the Boulton and Watt Collection of the Birmingham Public Library there is a photograph of one of these later machines in service. Neither the photograph nor the model machines can be accurately dated.

unnecessarily complex; certainly it was not up to Whitney's design. No method of adjustment vertically or transversely was provided, but since it was a rather specialized machine intended to produce a goodly number of identical pieces this was not required.

Nasmyth's machine does have a number of valuable features, however. The size and rugged construction of the machine are superior to the Whitney and the Middletown millers. The table is much larger, as would be required by the up-ending movement created by milling the nuts on "the spindle of a small dividing plate." [20]

The indexing feature is not new, for it had been developed far beyond this stage by French clock makers of the 18th century for gear cutting machinery. However, this is its first appearance on a milling machine, and it was not to appear again for this use until Howe's "universal" milling machine of 1850.

Nasmyth provided a mandrel "m" to adapt the fixture to any size nut. The small tank "l" provided a supply of water to the cutter "a" to keep it cool, the first evidence we have of the use of coolants in milling.

It seems clear that by about 1830 the principal elements of the milling machine had been introduced, some rather good design features had been developed, and at least a few men recognized the potentialities of this new tool — a machine far more useful, for light work at least, than the planer, and already in use in small arms manufacture. Certainly it was a machine capable of doing more rapidly and more precisely many operations which had previously required tedious and highly skilled hand work.

20. Nasmyth, *Autobiography*, p. 147.

II Interim: Whitney to Howe

GAY & SILVER

THE ARMORIES

ROBBINS & LAWRENCE

THE LINCOLN MILLER

ROBERTSON'S MILLER

FREDERICK W. HOWE

INTERIM: WHITNEY TO HOWE

The generation of milling machine designers after Whitney seems to be groping for the elements of a really satisfactory design, which was reached with the appearance of the Lincoln miller in 1855 for plain milling, but the versatility of the universal milling machine had to await the genius of Joseph R. Brown in 1861. However, as in so many other inventions, it is this period of groping that is of greatest interest in a study of the nature of technical innovation, for it is so often neglected by historians, but when carefully studied illustrates the universal law of history: that the great men are those who, at the right time, twist together into a strong rope the many threads spun by lesser men.

Gay & Silver

The first milling machine of this period of which we have any accurate information was one in the old Gay & Silver shop [1] in North Chelmsford, Massachusetts.

This miller was seen there still in use as late as 1908 and photographed [2] (Fig. 6). Dixie says that this was shown to him as "the first milling machine made in this country." This now seems unlikely, but the machine is difficult to date. Since it was in use for perhaps 75 years, no doubt many of its features are of a later date than the basic machine. Dixie says, "Originally the machine had hand feed only, but some genius added an automatic feed and stop." [3]

1. Later the North Chelmsford Machine and Supply Company. The early tools were apparently still there in 1916; the company went out of business and the tools were sold in 1920 or 1921. All efforts to trace them recently have failed.
2. E. A. Dixie, "Some More Antique Machine Tools," *American Machinist*, 1908, pp. 558-559.
3. Compare Dixie's photograph of 1908 with that of 1896 in *Machinery*, April 1896, p. 229, fig. 6, which clearly shows these additions to have been made after 1896. The main drive pulley had also been replaced. It did not take much of "genius" to add, after 1896, a power feed essentially that of Whitney's of about 1820!

Certain features of the Gay & Silver miller are, however, apparent from the photograph. The rather crude base on which it rests is more substantial and the general construction is more solid and heavier than any up to this time.

The means of securing the work to the table looks very much like that used in the Middletown machine. But this machine has two features we have not seen before: (a) provision for vertical adjustment of the cutter spindle, with what may be a means of clamping the head at the desired height, and (b) an overarm for support of the outer end of the cutter spindle.

FIG. 6. THE GAY & SILVER MILLER OF ABOUT 1835.
(*American Machinist*)

In trying to date this machine one is tempted to conclude too much from the fact that Frederick W. Howe, whose work on the milling machine was to be central throughout this period, learned his trade in the old Gay & Silver shop and was there after 1838. Possibly this is the machine which first inspired Howe's long interest in the design of the milling machine; perhaps it is even the first of his many remarkable designs. Certainly it embodies in crude form many of the features of Howe's later millers.

The Gay & Silver miller can perhaps be dated as not before 1830, the date Ira and Ziba Gay started the shop, and prior to March 1841 when their sales records indicated one sold to the Amoskeaog Land and Power Company.[4]

A much cruder machine of about this same period was the Ingersoll planer type, often called a "slabbing machine." This had a wooden base with iron ways on which the bed moved. Many of these slabbing machines had the table driven, as were the planers of the time, by a chain drive. The whole saddle of the machine, including its driving pulley and gears, was raised and lowered on a vertical post frame by means of a screw and bevel gear arrangement. The saddle provided support for the cutter *between* the two spindle bearings. While this machine was probably not capable of very accurate work, it did embody a number of features important for later design.[5]

The Armories

Early work on the milling machine was also being done in government armories. Records of the Springfield Armory, now in the National Archives, include a contract made in 1827 with Thomas Blanchard for the rights to his patent for a "stocking lathe" which he had built in 1818. The contract also includes rights to other machines Blanchard had already devised and built for use in making various parts of the locks for muskets. These machines are not described, only the metal parts on which they were used, some of which clearly required milling operations. A "Report on Inspection of the Springfield Armories" of 1801 says, ". . . some water machinery is now preparing which will diminish the demand of this expensive article" [files].[6] We could therefore safely

4. Anon., "Some Early Milling Machines," *Machinery*, April, 1896, p. 221.
5. See photo in *Machinery*, April, 1896, p. 229, fig. 1, and *American Machinist*, 1924, p. 256, figs. 84 and 85.
6. Reprinted in James E. Hicks, *United States Ordnance*, Vol. II, "Ordnance Correspondence," Mt. Vernon, New York, 1940, p. 131.

date Blanchard's machines as having been built between 1801 and 1818, but we cannot say precisely what they were like except that they were some kind of milling machine.

As early as 1819 John H. Hall was using some sort of milling machine at Harper's Ferry. At the Springfield Armory, the first milling machine clearly on record seems to have been a fixed-spindle machine used for rough flat-milling monkey wrenches in 1834. But at about this same time a plain milling machine was being devised there, for in 1835 the master-armorer at Springfield sent to get a Mr. Barker to build "a milling machine like those in use in the Middletown gun manufactures." This was evidently to be an improvement, for it had a lever adjustment of the distance of the cutter spindle above the work. It is said that about 1830 Ethan Allen devised the method of using formed cutters for milling parts of pistol locks. In 1840 Thomas Warner also built milling machines with vertical slides as in the "Lincoln" miller. Of the details of these machines we know little,[7] but it can at least be shown that milling machine progress was continuous from Whitney to Howe.

Robbins & Lawrence

The first milling machines clearly the design of Frederick W. Howe are those built by Robbins & Lawrence of Windsor, Vermont, from his design of 1848.[8] This was the prototype of the Lincoln miller.

7. Except what little can be inferred from an illustration in *Harper's Weekly*, Sept. 21, 1861, p. 605 showing a "planing machine" used at the Springfield Armory. It was evidently a kind of vertical milling machine, but the sketch is not sufficiently detailed to tell much more. See also Charles H. Fitch, "Interchangeable Manufactures," *Report on Manufactures of the U. S. Tenth Census of 1880*, Washington, GPO, 1883, pp. 2 and 25.

8. His original drawings are still in the possession of Jones & Lamson Machine Company of Springfield, Vermont. They are reproduced on p. 732 of the *American Machinist* for 1914. It is possible that Richard S. Lawrence collaborated in this design.

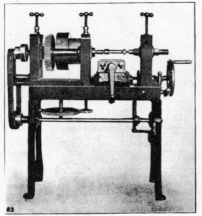

FIG. 7. HOWE'S ORIGINAL PLAIN MILLING MACHINE, 1848.
(*American Machinist*)

This Robbins & Lawrence miller (Fig. 7) represents further evolution in the direction of a machine capable of heavier work. The wider belt pulleys, mechanical advantage resembling back gearing from the pulley spindle to the cutter spindle, support of the outer end of the cutter spindle, and generally heavier construction throughout indicate a machine beginning to approach precision and at the same time capable of heavier work. It is, of course, still only a plain miller, but it did include a convenient screw mechanism by which the table could be moved by hand in cross feed and also a bolt and nut to clamp it in the desired position along the axis of the cutter spindle. Its power and hand feed are more rugged than any we have seen thus far, and are marred only by the use of a rack-and-pinion mechanism which chattered badly when starting a heavy cut. Whitney had had a better design, but it was not until F. A. Pratt's Lincoln miller that the screw-and-nut device was widely used in practice.[9]

9. In 1848, while superintendent of the Colt Armory in Hartford, E. K. Root had built a miller with a table driven by a worm engaging a spiral rack underneath the table. This machine also had a lever operated clutch to disengage the spindle from the drive and an automatic knock-off which stopped the machine instantly at any desired point in the feed.

Howe had not yet solved the problem of vertical adjustment of the cutter spindle, however. He used here an ingenious, but clumsy, method involving gears on the end of screws to raise and lower the spindle driving the cutter. Yet a separate control was provided for the bearing supporting the outer end of the cutter spindle. All this involved an equally ingenious method of driving the power feed from the spindle shaft. A similar method of vertical adjustment was retained on the Lincoln miller.

This particular problem was solved in 1854 when Root replaced the usual outer support with the overarm essentially as used today (Fig. 8). This produced an "open side" miller; the Lincoln was not.

The Lincoln Miller

The "Lincoln" miller took its name from the manufacturer who first brought it out in 1855, rather than from its designers, F. A. Pratt and E. K. Root, who quite clearly built upon the Robbins & Lawrence 1848 design of F. W. Howe, probably brought to Hartford by Richard S. Lawrence a

FIG. 8. ROOT'S MILLER OF 1854
     WITH OVERARM.
   (*American Machinist*)

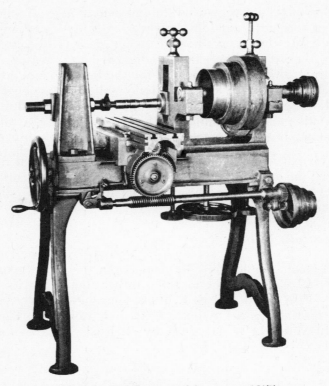

FIG. 9. THE LINCOLN MILLER OF 1855.
The first production milling machine.
(*Pratt & Whitney*)

year or two earlier.[10] Thousands of these millers were built
and sold all over the world — many of them built by the
firm founded by F. A. Pratt and Amos Whitney.

As is evident from Fig. 9 the Lincoln miller[11] did not
differ fundamentally from the Robbins & Lawrence 1848
miller of Howe except for Pratt's much more rugged and
compact design, and his replacement of the rack-and-pinion

10. Charles H. Fitch, "Interchangeable Manufactures," *Report on Manu-factures of the U. S. Tenth Census of 1880*, Washington, GPO, 1883, p. 25.
11. Two excellent examples of this type of miller are to be found in the Ford Museum, Dearborn, Michigan.

feed by the screw-and-nut method. Pratt was clearly the principal designer, but even he had not been able to solve adequately the problem of vertical adjustment of the cutter spindle.[12]

With the Lincoln miller this new tool comes to be of definite significance in metal-cutting production. The large numbers sold by several manufacturers, its widespread use in the production of light machinery in many industries — small arms, sewing machines, etc. — all testify to the fact that by 1860 the milling machine had an assured place in at least the American metal trades. It was of no little significance in providing the large number of small arms required for the Civil War.

Robertson's Miller

A milling machine of less economic importance, though of greater technical interest than the Lincoln miller, was Robertson's of 1852. This was the first milling machine to be patented in the United States.[13] It, too, was in use in the old Whitneyville shop, passed into the hands of the Winchester Repeating Arms Company, and was still in use in their plant when Roe photographed it there in 1912. It later passed into the custody of the Mason Mechanical Engineering Laboratory at Yale, and is now on permanent loan to the U. S. National Museum [14] (Fig. 10).

It has a power feed, not different in principle from Whitney's but more rugged and more convenient, with about 18½ inches of traverse. It also has a cross feed (3½″) mechanism in a saddle fitted to guides in the bed which supports the table. However, the power feed to the table is of the rack-and-pinion type. The table, its slide and gibs are heavy and well constructed to take a substantial load, as

12. *Machinery*, April, 1896, p. 222 and photo on p. 230. One curious and ingenious attempt was made by Sellers, rotating a large bushing in the head which carried the spindle eccentrically.
13. Patent No. 9,307 of October 5, 1852.
14. USNM Catalogue No. 314,939.

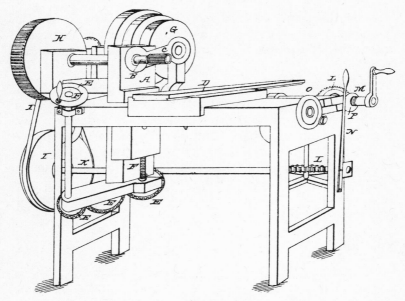

FIG. 10. ROBERTSON'S MILLER OF 1852.
(*U. S. Patent*)

is the general construction of the machine throughout. Although not shown in the patent the outer end of the cutter spindle may have been suppored by means similar to that used in the Lincoln miller. There are holes in the base suitable for a detachable support as shown for the Lincoln miller (Fig. 9), but if once fitted it is now lost.

What is of greatest technical interest in this machine is the clear departure from the Robbins & Lawrence and the Lincoln method of vertical adjustment of the cutter spindle and, in principle, a return to the Gay & Silver method: the whole assembly of cutter spindle, bearings, post and spindle drive gear is carried on a heavy vertical slide held by an adjustable nut and bolt clamp into a close fitting guide cast into the base of the machine. This vertical slide is moved up and down 5⅝″ by a convenient and rugged chain of gears to be seen under the guide in Fig. 10. A screw stop is provided on the vertical adjustment. The spindle drive

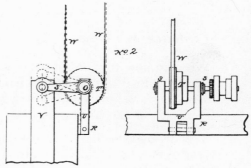

FIG. 11. DRIVE MECHANISM OF
ROBERTSON'S MILLER.
(*U. S. Patent*)

gear (Fig. 11) is kept engaged with the pinion on the pulley shaft by mounting the pulley shaft in a yoke capable of movement about a shaft supporting it. The yoke is connected to the spindle shaft bearings by two links. All in all, it was a very ingenious mechanism, and from its long years of service, evidently a satisfactory and practical one. Clearly Robertson's machine marks a technical advance over Pratt's Lincoln miller, even if it did not become as widely used.

FIG. 12. ROBBINS & LAWRENCE MILLING MACHINE, 1850.
(*American Machinist*)

Frederick W. Howe

We may now turn to the later work of Frederick W. Howe.
While still with Robbins & Lawrence, Howe designed in 1850
a milling machine which was probably the first ever manufactured for the trade (Fig. 12). Hubbard [15] describes it:

". . . has a massive four legged cast iron table, at the
rear of and beneath which are the drivers, cone pulleys, and
gears of the feeding mechanism. On the top of the table is
mounted the headstock, and at the front, the substantial
column carrying the work-holding chuck and the indexing
mechanism. Upon being unlocked, the column may be
raised and lowered by an elevating screw, operated by a
handwheel through a train of spur gears, and may be indexed
by means of a large horizontal index plate drilled with
numerous accurately spaced holes for the index pin, which
is held in a swinging arm.

"The horizontal spindle, upon which the drive pulley
is directly mounted, is arranged to have a short forward and
backward movement in the headstock, being operated by a
hand lever when the sliding spindle is unlocked. The entire
headstock is arranged to slide both crosswise and lengthwise
in ways on top of the table, their motions being imparted
by handwheels, or by power feeds acting upon feed screws
through bevel gears . . ." It could be fitted with an indexing
head.

This machine has a number of features which indicate
groping for a really sound design, and at the same time it
is a further over-refinement. Its principal interesting feature is that it is the first to have power cross feed.

15. Guy Hubbard, *American Machinist,* 1924, p. 257. The author cannot
agree with Mr. Hubbard that this machine can properly be called a "universal" milling machine, nor that this machine influenced Joseph R. Brown
in inventing his universal milling machine. On the contrary, it is based upon
quite different principles and is a very awkward piece of design not at all
compatible with the rest of Howe's work but anticipating in some features
his miller of 1852. One of these machines is still in service at Lamson &
Goodnow Mfg. Co., Shelburne Falls, Mass. After the Whitney machine this
is probably the oldest milling machine extant.

Howe designed in 1852 what was called a "universal miller." In a certain sense this designation was justified, but it has led to some controversy [16] because the universal milling machine invented by Joseph R. Brown in 1861 has fixed the meaning which the term now has in the minds of machinists everywhere. Howe's machine was certainly not "universal" in this sense at all, but it was a very creditable piece of design embodying a number of important advances (Fig. 13).

Howe's milling machine of 1852 is described by Burlingame: "to combine in a machine having a vertically adjustable cutter slide, a swiveling chuck in place of the usual work table; the work held in this chuck, which had its

FIG. 13. HOWE'S MILLING MA-
CHINE OF 1852.
(*American Machinist*)

16. Luther D. Burlingame, "The Development of Interchangeable Manufacture," *American Machinist*, 1914, p. 297. This article sets forth the facts clearly, concisely and correctly, although his drawing marked "fig. 2" is not of Brown as indicated in the text, nor is it indicated that Howe's original drawings show that they were made for the Newark Machine Company in 1857. The controversy between Burlingame and Guy Hubbard in the *Vermont Journal*, Windsor, Vermont, seems one of semantics. The author prefers to let the drawings and the photographs of the actual machines speak for themselves, for they give proper credit to both Howe and Brown.

axis in a vertical plane, could be revolved, indexed, swiveled in two planes or fed longitudinally under the cutter, so that the name 'universal' seems quite appropriate, although Mr. Howe's machine did not contain any of the vital elements of the present-day universal miller." [17]

Further details were given in *American Machinist*, 1895, page 270:

"To the bed, of box form, is fitted in front a saddle which was a horizontal movement (by hand or automatic) and carries a knee which can be tilted 15 or 20 degrees either way from the horizontal position and secured by bolts passing through curved slots. The knee supports the index, which can be rotated by the crank handle shown at the right, and can also be clamped in any position. To the face of the upright is fitted a saddle which has a vertical movement, and to this saddle is fitted the overhanging arm, this arm having a short horizontal movement for adjustment of cut. It has automatic, vertical and horizontal feeds . . ."

Howe's machine had a number of very good features. Until Brown's invention of the knee and column type it was the best design to meet the problem of vertical adjustment of the cutter — simple, rugged, flexible, and convenient. He included the overarm support of the cutter spindle, with adequate means of cross feed, and provided a power vertical feed. He also retained the screw-and-nut drive of the longitudinal feed and applied it to vertical and cross feed.

But Howe's machine is an example of the overly complex type of machine which usually closes a period of innovation and heralds the appearance of the definitive and simpler form — in this case Joseph R. Brown's Universal Milling Machine of 1861.

Two later contributions to milling machine design by Frederick W. Howe should first be noted. Howe left Robbins & Lawrence in 1856 and in 1861 became superintendent of the Providence Tool Company, Providence, Rhode Island.[18] It was while serving in this capacity that, in 1861,

17. See below p. 50 for the significant features of Brown's universal miller.
18. Guy Hubbard, *American Machinist*, 1924, p. 439.

FIG. 14. THE PROVIDENCE TOOL COMPANY'S MILLING MACHINE.
With a formed rotary file cutter used on it.
(*Scientific American*)

he asked Joseph R. Brown to design the machine which was to be the Universal Milling Machine. In 1863 the Providence Tool Company brought out a much simpler type of plain milling machine (Fig. 14), almost certainly the design of Howe.[19] It embodied a number of interesting features: (a) the use of an automatic throw-out of the power feed by means of a stop which could be bolted at the desired point in a slot on the side of the table, a device still to be found on many modern milling machines as well as on other types of machine tools, (b) an oil pan was cast into the bed of the machine to keep chips, oil, etc., off the floor, (c) an overarm was provided for use on heavy cuts.

But two features of this design are of greater interest. First, is the method of vertical adjustment, one still incorporated, usually in addition to vertical control of the knee, in a number of modern milling machines.[20] This consists of

19. *Scientific American*, 1863, p. 321. Although it bears a very close resemblance to a plain miller of Bement & Dougherty Industrial Works of Philadelphia (of which a photograph and a drawing dated September 28, 1861, are in the files of Brown & Sharpe). The rights to build this machine were secured, and it was for many years built by Brown & Sharpe as their No. 13 Plain Milling Machine.
20. Brown & Sharpe No. 1 Plain Milling Machine very closely resembled the Providence miller; and their No. 2 and No. 3 Plain Milling Machines utilized this same principle, combined with the overarm of Root. See Brown & Sharpe Company, *Treatise on Milling Machines*, Providence, R. I., 1893.

mounting the cutter spindle, its bearings and its driving gear on two heavy arms which are keyed onto a shaft carried in bearings in a heavy elbow upright. The vertical adjustment of the spindle is provided by a vertical screw passing through a heavy boss on the nearer arm and carrying two adjusting nuts, which can of course be locked against each other. This method was simple, precise and also did not require readjustment of belt tension with each vertical change. It was altogether a very neat and workable design.

The cutters shown as used on this machine for milling the lock plate on a musket are also of great interest, for they show the old rotary-file type of cutter still in use, but now developed into a rather complex *formed* cutter. However, the cutters shown on the machine itself indicate clearly that by this time plain cutters, with coarse teeth, each one of which would take a substantial chip, were also in use.

One other machine of Howe's deserves to be mentioned, if only because it was the only one to which his name became commonly attached and the only one to have a really extensive sale. This he designed while he was a mechanical engineer for Brown & Sharpe Company from 1868 to 1873. It was for many years listed in their catalogue as the "No. 12 plain milling machine" and was known to the trade as the "Howe Miller."

The Providence Tool Company miller and the Brown & Sharpe No. 12 plain miller indicate that Howe clearly had gone on from the stage of groping for adequate design to milling machines of the simplicity, convenience, and flexibility that indicate technical maturity. Howe had struggled with the problems of the milling machine for a lifetime. The genius of Joseph R. Brown was to bring that struggle to a triumphant climax.

III Joseph R. Brown and
the Universal Milling Machine

THE FIRST UNIVERSAL
MILLING MACHINE

EARLY MILLING CUTTERS

JOSEPH R. BROWN AND THE
UNIVERSAL MILLING MACHINE

The basic story of the invention in 1861 of the Universal Milling Machine by Joseph R. Brown of the Brown & Sharpe Company, Providence, Rhode Island, has been ably told by Luther D. Burlingame of that firm.[1] The machine was invented by Brown at the suggestion of Frederick W. Howe to solve an immediate problem — the machining of the grooves on twist drills, to replace the slow and expensive process of filing them out of rod by hand. Brown's Universal Milling Machine was not only an ideal solution to Howe's drill problem, it could also be used for other kinds of spiral milling, for gear cutting and other work, up to this time done by hand at considerable expense. But it is doubtful if even Brown realized how epochmaking his invention was to become. It is significant of Brown's genius that he invented a machine of far wider application and one which embodies nearly all the basic features of milling machines to this day.

The First Universal Milling Machine

The historian is particularly fortunate that the interest of the Sharpe family led them to seek out and recover the first Brown & Sharpe Universal Milling Machine manufactured and to preserve it in the honored place it deserves in their collection of early machine tools.[2] It is also fortunate that Brown & Sharpe Company has preserved Brown's own drawings[3] of the machine (Fig. 15) dating from October

1. *American Machinist,* 1911, pp. 9-13. *Iron Trade Review,* 1915, pp. 923-926. The author has made use of much unpublished material collected largely by Luther D. Burlingame, now in the files of Brown and Sharpe. This material has proved invaluable in tracing the development of the milling machine from 1861.
2. A photograph of this machine is to be found opposite page 208 of Roe.
3. Note Brown's design of the frame to give rigidity far greater than that of previous millers.

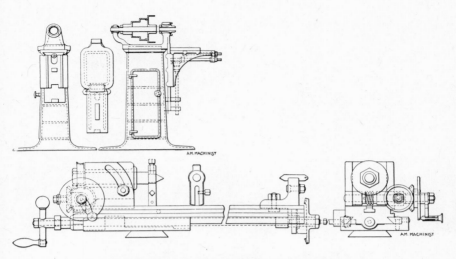

FIG. 15. UNIVERSAL MILLER FROM ORIGINAL DRAWING
BY JOSEPH R. BROWN, 1861.
(*Brown & Sharpe*)

1861 and September 7, 1862, as well as the original patent
drawings.[4] The first published account of the machine was
in the *Scientific American* of December 27, 1862 (Fig. 16).

". . . The frame A is cast hollow in one piece and has
shelves also cast in it, forming a cupboard to hold tools.

"In the upper part of the frame is the main arbor 'a,'
made of steel, running in a Babbitt-metal box with an anti-
friction curve at the front [5] and in a straight, bronze box at
the rear end; it can be closed up to compensate for wear.
. . . Upon the front side of the frame, A, a knee, C, is fitted
to slide, which can be moved by a screw, b, connecting it
with a projection from the frame. This screw is vertical and
is connected with a horizontal shaft by beveled gears, being
operated by a crank on the squared end of the horizontal
shaft, c, that projects from the forward part of the knee. Behind this vertical screw, is another rod, d, which is attached
firmly to the knee, and passes freely through a hole in the
same projection in front of the frame which answers as a

4. Patent No. 46,521 of February 21, 1865.
5. At this time such bearings were believed to be of great value.

45

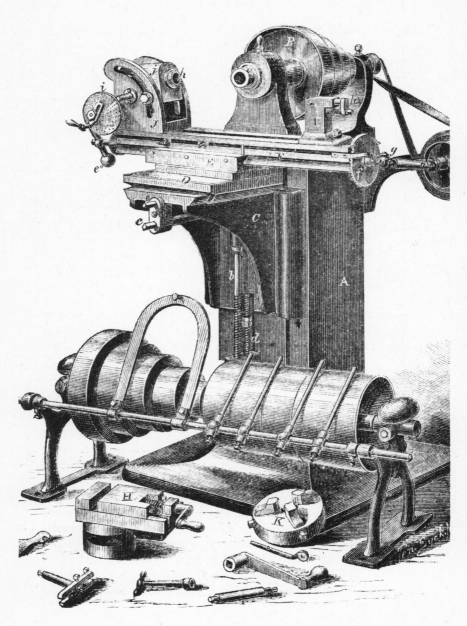

Fig. 16. The First Universal Milling Machine,
Brown & Sharpe, 1861.
(*Scientific American*)

nut for the first named screw. This constitutes a stop motion which limits the use of all of the knee and through it the depth to which the work is milled.[6]

"Upon the top of the knee C, a slide, D, is fitted, on a line parallel with the main arbor, to be moved by the screw, e. To the upper part of this siding piece of the casting, E, is attached, that moves [rotates] on its center horizontally only, a graduated arc showing its position. This piece can be clamped very firmly to the one below it. In this also the long carriage, F, . . . is fitted to slide, and is moved in the usual way by a screw working through a nut in it with a handle, e″, on one end. On the opposite end is a bevel geer [sic], f, connecting with another on a short shaft projecting from the side of the carriage. A connection is made between this short shaft and that of the feed cone, G, by two Hook's [sic] joints, g, and a shaft between them, made of two pieces, one sliding into the other with a feather let into one of them so that their relative [angular] positions may not be changed. This feeding arrangement is thrown in or out, by a lever, and can be set to stop it at any point. A vise, H, . . . is provided, which can be attached to the carriage, F, thereby rendering the tool equivalent to a plain milling machine with the advantage of being able to feed the carriage at any angle.

"At one end of the carriage is a stand, I, fitted to slide in a groove, with a center, 'h', in its top; this stand can be fastened at any point; opposite to it is a head, J, having a hollow arbor, h, in which a centre can be placed to be on a line with the centre 'h,' in the stand described. Between these centres is placed the work to be milled, in which any variation of spiral or its equivalent can be made by means of the index i, on the side of the head that is connected with

6. This rod, d, will be seen to be threaded and to carry stop nuts on it. It is the first clear use of this principle on milling machines, but was an early addition, since the first manufactured machine, in the Brown and Sharpe collection, does not have this feature. It is, however, shown on the drawings of September 7, 1862. The first machine has at present a single stop nut on the elevating screw, but this may be a later addition. Neither stop feature is referred to in the first patent of 1865.

47

the arbor by two miter gears, a worm, and worm wheel. The arbor in the head can also be connected with the screw that moves the carriage by spur wheels engaging with the miter gears and worm wheel just mentioned. When this is done, the arbor, h, revolves as the carriage advances, and thus gives a spiral motion to any piece held between the centres or on an arbor in the head. Changes or spur gears are furnished by which any spiral can be obtained. The machine ordinarily cuts right hand spirals, but by inserting an extra gear a left hand motion can be given to it. The part, j, of the head, J, supporting the arbor, can be raised to any angle and set, by divisions upon the arc through which it moves.[7] This arrangement renders the cutting of tapering spirals as easy as straight ones.[8] It can also be depressed below the line of the centres for the purpose of cutting the teeth in tapering rimers [reamers]. A small universal chuck, K, is fitted to screw on the arbor, h, . . . for cutting face mills, or doing any work on or near the ends of small cylindrical pieces. . . ."[9]

This detailed description of Brown's machine is justified by such a fundamental advance and by its significance for all later milling machines. It incorporates many advances: increased power and rigidity, improved feed (although not the final form), more adequate cross feed, use of stop nuts, at least on the vertical motion, but most of all, the intro-

7. Note that these and the following features were not at all required by the problem Howe set Brown for the grooving of drills. They were included by Brown to make the machine of much wider application, as indicated in the text. They quite clearly grew out of Brown's earlier work on machines for cutting bevel gears.

8. See Besson's screw-cutting lathe of 1578, as shown in *Theatrum instrumentorum et machinarum Jacobi Bessoni Delphinatis, Mathematici ingeniosissime,* Lugduni, apud Barth. Vincentium, 1578, fig. 9.

9. By at least as early as 1867 Brown had added, for the first time on any machine tool, the use of micrometer dials reading to thousandths; on both the cross feed and the vertical movement screw connections there were graduated circles on a plate and a pointer behind the crank to indicate the setting on these graduations. (See Brown & Sharpe Catalogue of May 15, 1867, p. 5.) The adjustable dials were also first introduced by Brown & Sharpe on their machines about 1885.

FIG. 17. GARVIN'S NO. 4 MILL-
ING MACHINE, 1880.
Combining the overarm with
the knee and column support
of the table.

(*American Machinist*)

duction of the column and knee principle [10] as the final solution to the problem of vertical adjustment of the cutter
relative to the work. To be sure, Brown provided no support
for the outer end of the cutter spindle, either of the Lincoln
type or of Root's overarm. But his machine was intended
only for light work. The knee and column principle was first
combined with the overarm at about this same time in the
Garvin Plain Milling Machine, (Fig. 17) as "the prototype
of the column and knee of the present day." [11]

As the demand developed for a machine capable of
heavier work, such as for steam engine and locomotive work,
Brown & Sharpe brought out a larger size of universal milling machine which was first exhibited at the Centennial
Exposition of 1876 (Fig. 18). This machine was similar to
the machine of 1862 with the addition of back gears, and an

10. Anticipated by John George Bodmer of Manchester, England, in his
patent of 1839 (British patent No. 8070) which had, however, little subsequent influence. It should be noted, however, that various forms of knee-
and-column tables had been used in drill presses before Bodmer.

11. Sol Einstein, *Forty Years of Milling Machine Development by the
Cincinnati Milling Machine Company,* unpublished typescript of June 23,
1923, in the files of the Cincinnati Milling Machine Company, Cincinnati,
Ohio.

FIG. 18. BROWN & SHARPE'S
LARGE UNIVERSAL MILLING
MACHINE OF 1876.
(*Wilson*)

overarm, but was about double the size.[12] Until the expiration of Brown's original patent of 1865 these were the only two universal milling machines on the market.[13]

The features of Brown's Universal Milling Machine which were really new were:

"1. Having the table carried in a swiveling saddle mounted on a clamp bed which in turn has a traverse movement on the vertically adjustable knee.

"2. A spiral head mounted on a sliding table and connected to the feed screw to cut spirals and with provision for indexing.

"3. Means for adjusting the spiral head so that when set at an angle it can be indexed." [14]

Brown's machine incorporated in a single synthesis the valuable results of the whole development since Whitney, but it was these features which made Brown's miller a truly "universal" machine, one of great flexibility and therefore the ancestor of the milling machine as we know it today.

12. Joseph M. Wilson, *Masterpieces of the Centennial International Exhibition 1876*, Philadelphia, n.d., Vol. III, pp. 145-149.

13. L. D. Burlingame, *American Machinist*, 1911, p. 11.

14. L. D. Burlingame, *History of Milling Machine Features*, unpublished typescript in Brown & Sharpe files.

Early Milling Cutters

At this point we can conveniently leave the development of the milling machine proper and look into its most important feature — the cutter. Here, too, we shall find that Joseph R. Brown brings the earlier development to a climax and charts the course which later improvements were to follow.

The French clockmakers of the mid-18th century had used a form of milling cutter for machining the teeth on gear wheels for clocks.[15] The earliest of these now extant are to be found in the Conservatoire des Arts et Métiers.[16] These cutters are rather small and are really rotary files rather than milling cutters as we commonly think of them. A large one made by Vaucanson prior to 1782 was presented to Lucien Sharpe of the Brown & Sharpe Company about 60 years ago by a former official of the Conservatoire des Arts et Métiers, M. F. G. Kreutzberger[17] and has been preserved by them in a block of clear plastic (Fig. 3). It is clearly a formed gear cutter with teeth resembling those of a coarse rotary file, apparently chipped out by hand. As indicated earlier, there is little reason to believe that milling cutters prior to 1850 were even as advanced as this, rather they were probably simple cylindrical cutters having the same file-like teeth. In any case, until the early 1850's the cutters are all basically files in that they cut very fine chips from the work rather than the substantial chip removed by a lathe, a planer, or a milling machine of Brown's day.[18]

There seems to have been a gradual process by which milling cutters were made with coarser teeth. The oldest one we have with teeth which would clearly take a sub-

15. See above p. 12.
16. *Catalogue Officiel des Collections*, Vol. 3, Paris, 1906, pp. 156-161.
17. L. D. Burlingame, *Iron Trade Review*, 1915, p. 923.
18. But Bodmer's patent of 1839 shows one clearly having coarse teeth, and Rehé's gear-cutting engine of 1783 had a coarse tooth cutter. Rehé also provided a machine for grinding these cutters accurately. Note also the very modern looking cutters of Willis' machine (p. 24 and Fig. 4).

FIG. 19. A MILLING
CUTTER OF ABOUT 1850.
(*American Machinist*)

stantial chip was that made by the Phoenix Iron Works of
Hartford, Connecticut and was used in gear cutting machines about 1850 [19] (Fig. 19). It was $2^{15}/_{16}$ in. outside diameter, ⅞ in. inside diameter, $2^{3}/_{64}$ in. thick and had 56 teeth.
It had formed teeth chipped by chisel and hammer. To
sharpen these cutters they were first annealed; the faces of
the teeth were then peened or upset with a drift. The cutter
was then rotated backwards on a mandrel and turned to
proper form to fit a sheet metal template. Clearance was
then filed on the teeth and the cutter again hardened. A
number of these cutters for the different pitches were kept
on hand, together with the sheet-metal gages for forming
them. Their principal defect was, of course, the great cost
in labor and time in sharpening them.

The solution to this problem was provided in 1864 with
Joseph R. Brown's patent [20] for a formed cutter which could
be ground on its face without changing its shape (Fig. 20).
It was described thus in the inventor's specification:

"My invention relates to an improvement in the teeth or
cutting blades of the rotary cutter which is generally used

19. E. A. Dixie, *American Machinist*, 1913, p. 491.
20. Patent No. 45,294 of November 29, 1864.

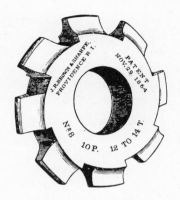

FIG. 20. BROWN'S CUTTER OF 1864.
(*Brown & Sharpe*)

for cutting the teeth of gears, and is calculated to remedy
an important difficulty that I will mention. Ordinarily the
teeth or blades of the cutter are filed up[21] to a cutting edge
in quite an imperfect manner, and as the requisite clearance
in such teeth or blades is considerable any subsequent sharpening of the teeth reduces their cutting contour[22] so mate-
rially as to alter both the size and form of the teeth which
they are intended to cut, and this renders the cutter useless.
My improvement to overcome this difficulty, consists in con-
structing the teeth or blades in the form of segments or
curvilinear sections that are mechanically accurate in outline
and of equal size and contour throughout their entire length,
each of which has a sufficient circumferential inclination
with respect to the revolving circumference of the cutter to
produce the proper degree of clearance, so that the tooth
may be sharpened by grinding away its face until the
strength of the tooth is permanently impaired and always
present the same cutting contour, each new face and cutting
edge produced by grinding being a fresh radial section of
an equiform tooth throughout its whole length."

21. This would suggest that between the Phoenix Iron Works cutter and
1864, cutters had been produced having coarser teeth and of a form such
that they could be sharpened by filing. The author has seen such cutters
and their templates in the collection of Lamson & Goodnow, but these cannot
be accurately dated.
22. For the development of the form of gear teeth, see R. S. Woodbury,
History of the Gear-Cutting Machine, The Technology Press, Cambridge,
Mass., 1958.

As with the universal milling machine, Brown's patented formed cutter marked the culmination of a development [23] and the prototype of what was to come. At any rate, the next few years show patents of all the principal types of cutters appearing rapidly. A spiral cutter had been patented as early as 1856.[24] Developments after Brown are:

irregular spacing of teeth (1867),[25]
notched teeth (1869),[26]
forms of inserted teeth (1872),[27]
spiral groove for breaking up the cut (1881),[28]
face milling cutter with inserted teeth (1884),[29]
alternate teeth of different shape (1895),[30]
inserted tooth spiral cutter (1900),[31]
teeth cutting on alternate sides
    with one full tooth (1902),[32]
cutters for saws with alternate teeth cutting (1907).[33]

Other cutters especially designed for gears should be mentioned: Clough's "box cutters" of 1885,[34] and the Step Roughing Cutter of 1907.[35] The general trend in milling cutters has been in the direction of increased strength and precision, and efforts to relieve vibration. For many purposes fewer teeth have been used, especially after the intro-

23. One which we are, unfortunately, unable to trace in detail for lack of evidence.
24. Patent O. Moses, No. 15,342 of July 15, 1856 for a straw cutter. Brown & Sharpe Catalogue for 1877 shows them for metalworking, and they had probably been used earlier. Patent George Bechtol, No. 512,463 of January 9, 1894.
25. Patent H. N. Keables, No. 66,354 of July 2, 1867.
26. Patent Lutz and Reiss, No. 93,212 of August 3, 1869.
27. Note that this had been done by Rehé as early as 1783 (see Woodbury, Gear-Cutting Machine, p. 54). Also at Leeds as early as 1848. See above p. 24.
28. British patent, Alfred Muir, Manchester, England, No. 498 of August 1, 1881.
29. French patent of March 17, 1884, issued to MM. Heilmann, Ducomneun, and Steinlein, of Mulhouse, Alsace.
30. Patent George B. Beal, No. 543,608 of July 30, 1895.
31. Patent John W. Boynton, No. 650,924 of June 5, 1900.
32. B. W. M. Hanson, Iron Trade Review, August 21, 1902, p. 34.
33. Patent Charles Napier, No. 842,903 of February 5, 1907.
34. Patent R. M. Clough, No. 329,721 of November 3, 1885.
35. American Machinist, 1910, p. 488.

FIG. 21. TYPES OF MODERN MILLING CUTTERS.
(*Cincinnati*)

duction of the vertical spindle milling machine brought about wider use of end mill and "fly cutter" types.[36]

Today there are a bewildering variety of milling and gear cutters for general use as well as thousands of specialized types (Fig. 21). The increasing variety and the precision of sharpening required by milling cutters soon required specialized means of grinding them — the Cutter Grinder.[37]

By 1865 the work of Joseph R. Brown had set the stage for further development and exploration of the possibilities inherent in the milling machine as he left it. These included much greater convenience in operation, greater strength and rigidity, application of the electric motor, and automatic operation — all characteristics which led to more widespread use of this machine in industry because of its greater capabilities and flexibility. Few metal-cutting manufacturing processes failed to find a use for this versatile machine tool.

36. See Patent L. Griswold, No. 111,927 of February 21, 1871 for early evidence of the fly cutter type.

37. This development will be taken up in a later monograph, the *History of the Metal-Cutting Process and Its Tools.*

IV Further Growth —
Strength, Convenience and
Constant Speed

FURTHER GROWTH [1]

STRENGTH, CONVENIENCE AND CONSTANT SPEED

In the technical development [2] of the milling machine, after Joseph R. Brown had given it its basic form, the most interesting and significant features are the feed mechanisms and their control, and the prime mover and its connections to the spindle, but they are only the most important parts of a whole series of improvements which created the modern milling machine.

General Features

Up to 1900 milling machines were built from the floor up, although Brown & Sharpe had begun in the 1860's to build them in batches rather than to build each machine to order. However, the development of many different types of drive, control, etc., made felt the need for some type of standardization in manufacture for convenience in production and for assembly of the desired type from standard parts. Unit construction was so evidently needed by 1900 that both John Parker at Brown & Sharpe and Fred Holz at Cincinnati Milling Machine Company applied almost simultaneously for patents utilizing this idea. Parker's patent was, however, the later of the two and was not as specific regarding unit construction since it was primarily a patent on a variable speed gear, which was not actually used by Brown & Sharpe.

1. In this section the author has made use of two unpublished papers in the files of Brown & Sharpe by L. D. Burlingame, *Milling Machine Evolution* and *History of Milling Machine Features,* as well as Sol Einstein's unpublished paper in the files of the Cincinnati Milling Machine Company referred to above. Use has also been made of much other material from the files of the Cincinnati Milling Machine Company.

2. Readers interested in detailed drawings of many of these machines can find them in Joseph Horner, *Modern Milling Machines, London,* 1906.

The patent of Fred Holz described a feed mechanism composed of units to be bolted to the frame and involved a unit construction actually used in Cincinnati milling machines from that time on.[3] Unit construction and interchangeable frames were more specifically claimed in A. L. De Leeuw's patent No. 980,614 of January 3, 1911. After several years of experimental work by Fred Holz the principle of unit construction was embodied in the Cincinnati "High Power" milling machines introduced 1907-1908 (Fig. 22).[4] This

3. Patent John Parker, No. 682,227 of September 10, 1901 (application, August 29, 1900), and patent Fred Holz, No. 658,777 of Ooctober 2, 1900 (application, March 26, 1900).

4. *American Machinist,* 1908, pp. 401-410.

FIG. 22. CINCINNATI HIGH POWER UNIVERSAL MILLING MACHINE OF 1908.
Variable speed motor drive, feed drive in inches
per revolution, and unit type construction.
(*Cincinnati*)

2536

FIG. 23. COMBINATIONS OF BASIC AND COMPLEMENTARY STANDARD
UNITS TO MEET VARIOUS MILLING NEEDS, 1927.
These are the first standard millers to have hydraulic controls.
(*Cincinnati*)

same type of construction was used in their automatic machines by 1913 and in their hydramatics of 1927. The unit principle was extended to other features than the feed drive until standard basic and complementary units permitted a combination capable of giving a milling machine to meet almost any requirements simply by selecting the desired units (Fig. 23).

Brown & Sharpe also introduced a feature designed by C. R. Gabriel, October 10, 1898 [5] by which double telescopic slides were provided to cover the openings in the knee resulting from cross feed. These were intended to keep chips, dirt, etc., out of the various knee mechanisms. They also provided in 1900 on their No. 24 Plain Milling Machine the convenience of clamping the knee from the front. [6] Brown & Sharpe also extended the ways above the top of the knee about 1890.

Two other improvements in knee design were made — the use of a stationary knee screw with a revolving nut for vertical adjustment, [7] and the telescopic knee screw to give sufficient vertical adjustment without making a hole in the floor to accommodate the knee screw. This appeared first in a French machine by Prétot shown at the "Exposition Universelle Internationale" of 1889. [8]

Stand

It will be remembered that the original Brown Universal Milling Machine had a stand consisting of a single hollow frame casting. This produced a very rigid frame and pro-

5. Not patented until claim of J. B. Foote, No. 745,431 of December 1, 1903. A kind of sliding guard had been used for this purpose after 1883. See Brown & Sharpe Catalogue of 1883, p. 3.

6. Later patented by Alfred Herbert et al., British patent No. 15,645 of July 8, 1907.

7. Patent A. D. Pentz, No. 461,202 of October 13, 1891.

8. *Reports of the U. S. Commissioners to the Universal Exposition of 1889 at Paris*, Washington, Vol. 3, 1891, pp. 333-334.

vided a convenient cupboard. The cupboard feature had been invented by W. B. Bement of Bement & Dougherty, Philadelphia, and was used by Brown & Sharpe under his patent.[9] This hollow construction later provided space to put the motor to give it full protection. This was done for grinding machines as early as May 1916 by both Brown & Sharpe and Abrasive Machine Tool Company, and in 1919 this feature was widely adopted in milling machines by many manufacturers.[10]

Overarm and Braces [11]

We have seen the concern of the designers of the early milling machines with providing support for the outer end of the cutter spindle, beginning with the Gay & Silver machine of about 1835. The first machine to incorporate the cylindrical overarm was E. K. Root's modification in 1854 of the Lincoln miller.[12] The first cylindrical sliding arm was patented [13] by L. Cosgrove and used on Brown & Sharpe machines.

As the work done on the milling machine grew heavier there were a number of attempts to provide still greater rigidity for the overarm. There was the double arm brought out by Kearney & Trecker.[14] This, of course, had the advantage of keeping the milling machine "open-ended." An arm of more rigid form was produced by Otto Mergenthaler [15] by use of a massive casting for the overarm (Fig. 24). The box type overarm to give maximum rigidity was

9. Patent No. 35,433 of June 3, 1862.

10. By Brown & Sharpe in machines made for Western Electric. By Cincinnati Milling Machine Company and Kearney & Trecker in machines made for Ford.

11. For a very detailed account with drawings and photos see L. D. Burlingame, *Machinery*, 1918, pp. 990-996.

12. See above p. 33 and Fig. 8.

13. Patent No. 282,704 of August 17, 1883.

14. Patent No. 1,053,296 of February 18, 1913, but used in a French design by Vautier in 1904.

15. Patent No. 636,914 of November 14, 1899. Anticipated, however, by A. H. Brainard's patent No. 131,733 of October 1, 1872.

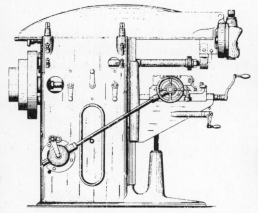

FIG. 24. MERGENTHALER'S MILL-
ING MACHINE OF 1898.
All-geared drive and an especially strengthened overarm
casting, as well as a vertical
spindle.
(*U. S. Patent*)

FIG. 25. BROWN & SHARPE NO. 5
PLAIN MILLING MACHINE OF 1898.
Note the overarm and braces.
(*Brown & Sharpe*)

first proposed by Professor John Sweet in 1904. After some
discussion of its merits it was adopted in all Cincinnati milling machines in the form later patented by A. L. De Leeuw
(Fig. 43).[16]

However, the great demands for rigidity of the cutter
spindle sometimes required sacrifice of the "open-end" feature and the use of devices to tie together the base, knee and
spindle. One of the earliest designs was that of John E.
Sweet in 1864 and produced by the Sweet & Barnes Company of Syracuse, New York. It had a massive casting ex-
tending from the outer end of the cutter spindle directly to
the base of the machine.[17]

Braces tying the outer end of the spindle to the knee
originated with Charles H. Phillips[18] (Fig. 25). The familiar

16. *Trans. Am. Soc. Mech. Eng.*, 1904, p. 100; *American Machinist*, 1904,
p. 130; *Engineer*, 1904, pp. 42 and 49. De Leeuw's patent No. 1,147,615 of
July 20, 1915.

17. See his letter of February 21, 1914, to Brown & Sharpe in their files,
together with photo.

18. Patent No. 484,455 of October 18, 1892. See also Fred Horner in
Machinery, July 1911, pp. 872-876.

form of overarm brace adjustable by means of slots, originated in 1896 with Fred Holz and was installed in Cincinnati millers (Figs. 22, 23, 25, and 43). Later designs were made by O. Hoppe of Switzerland.[19]

Brown & Sharpe added a projecting column which extended the inner arbor support *over* the table. This not only increased rigidity but allowed greater swivel of the table, with increased flexibility of the machine as a whole.[20]

Spindle Drive

One of the most important of the later advances in the milling machine was the *constant speed drive* and its associated features — geometrical progression of both feeds and speeds, feeds independent of spindle speeds, positive driving connections for spindle and feed, and the application of electric motor drive. Here again we see the influence of manufacturing needs for milling machines capable of doing heavier work. The earlier universal milling machine had been designed for toolroom work with light cuts; its drive and feed belts, like the whole machine, were proportioned accordingly. At first with the plain miller, drive belts and pulleys were widened and feeds were partially geared. Back gears were added in some machines. Many of these features may be seen in the Brown & Sharpe machine of 1876 (Fig. 18). By 1898 plain milling machines were available having double back gears, positive feed by chain and gearing, and feed and spindle speeds in geometrical progression (Fig. 25). Brown & Sharpe had used geometrical progression of spindle and feed speeds in belt driven machines prior to their development for lathes through gear trains in 1895 by Carl Barth. The first all-geared feed in a milling machine was shown in Henry M. Leland's patent of 1895.

More convenient means of changing gears by means of a single lever was introduced in an Austrian machine at the

19. U. S. Patents Nos. 1,419,853 of June 13, 1922 and 1,423,563 of July 25, 1922.
20. Patent B. P. Graves, No. 2,110,295 of March 8, 1938.

Paris Exposition of 1900. It was further developed by John Parker of Brown & Sharpe.[21] Further improvement of this feature was made by A. L. De Leeuw of Cincinnati Milling Machine Company.[22] The use of back gears themselves was improved by "having back gears at the front," in which the power is transmitted to the spindle near the front end. This method had been previously developed for lathes[23] but was put into milling machines without prior knowledge.[24]

Before 1900, however, the idea of an all-geared spindle drive to remove the inconvenience of belt shifting had made some progress. In 1898 O. Mergenthaler designed a machine[25] having a spindle driven by triple back gears and having all-geared feed. The feed was partially independent of the spindle speed because it was unaffected by back gear changes, but was dependent on change of belt on the three step driving cone (Fig. 24).

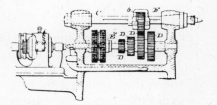

FIG. 26. W. P. NORTON'S CONSTANT SPEED TUMBLER-GEAR DRIVE, 1900. For the spindle of a lathe. Suited to either belt or motor drive.

(*U. S. Patent*)

In the early 90's W. P. Norton developed for the Hendey Machine Company an all-geared quick-shift feed train for lathes. Further work produced an all-geared drive lathe spindle by 1900.[26] This was the first all-geared drive and feed for a machine tool, which was suited to either belt or motor drive. (Fig. 26)

21. Patent No. 855,608 of May 28, 1907.
22. Patent No. 911,951 of February 9, 1909.
23. Patents B. G. Luther, No. 446,233 of February 10, 1891 and H. Bertram, No. 862,437 of August 6, 1907.
24. For Brown & Sharpe use, see *American Machinist*, October 22, 1903, pp. 1481-83. Patent Cincinnati Milling Machine Company (A. L. De Leeuw), No. 911,951 of February 9, 1909 (application, October 7, 1907).
25. Patent No. 636,914 of November 14, 1899 (application, May 11, 1898).
26. Patent No. 691,963 of January 28, 1902 (application, November 3, 1900).

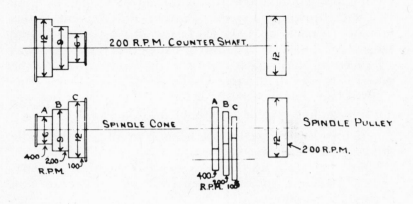

FIG. 27. PARKER'S MEMO OF 1900. THE BEGINNING
OF CONSTANT SPEED DRIVE
(Brown & Sharpe)

The first application of all-geared drive and feed to a milling machine was made at about this same time with the Brown & Sharpe constant speed milling machine. This had been designed in July of 1900 by John Parker whose memorandum signed December 14, 1900 applies to the drawing shown in Fig. 27.[27]

"When belt is on 'A' we are using a cutter one quarter the size as when belt is on 'C'; this is because the periphery speed of the cutter must be the same, regardless of the diameter.

"The periphery speed of belt, when on 'A', is 200 x 12 and of 'C' 200 x 6; thus, 'C' = ½ of 'A'. Yet it should be four times greater, as the cutter is four times larger, which means that the leverage to retard the cutter from revolving is four times more when using 'C' than when using 'A'. The machines now made are a compromise giving too much power on small cutters, and too little on large cutters.

27. Both drawing and memo are in the files of Brown & Sharpe.

"For comparison with the new method assume we need the same speeds on spindles as we have with the old method, viz: 100, 200, and 400, then the ratio of gearing would be A — 2 : 1, B — 1 : 1, and C — 1 : 2. This means we gear up for small mills when we do not need the power and gear down for large mills when we need the power.

"Another advantage in using the single pulley is that we can use the same size pulley above as below, viz: 12"; this gives us more belt contact, and greater leverage, which adds to the driving efficiency.

". . . The following is a method for obtaining a finer feed per revolution of spindle when using small end mills and a coarser feed per revolution of spindle when using large face mills than we can with our present milling machines. . . .[28]

"The proposed method is to take the feed from a single speed member in the spindle head (This member not to be affected by the spindle changes). This would give a range of feeds from ½" to 8" per minute with a ratio of 16 to 1.

"By my construction I dispense entirely with the cone pulley on the spindle. In addition I have the further advantage that by the employment of a Constant Speed Drive it is possible to connect a cutter-carrying spindle by variable speed gearing, and to connect the feed of the work table by means of other variable speed gearing whereby the speed of the spindle may be varied without correspondingly varying the speed of the work table." [29]

Others had recognized the need, and the correct solution had been suggested before Parker, but it was he who grasped the whole problem and designed the first milling machine to apply these principles correctly (Fig. 28).[30]

The constant speed drive needed a few additional conveniences: means for revolving the spindle by hand when

28. Note that this development was also influenced by the introduction of the many different types of milling cutters.
29. Note that Parker already has clearly in mind the advantage of independent spindle and feed speeds.

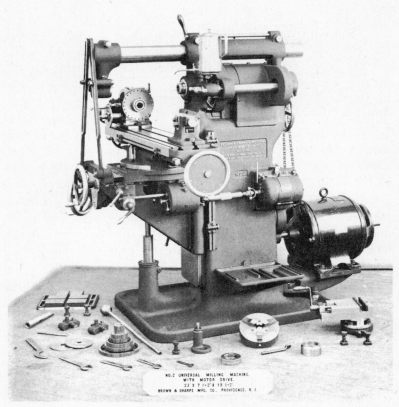

FIG. 28. BROWN & SHARPE'S NO. 2 UNIVERSAL MILLING MACHINE, 1901.
The first to have all-gear constant speed drive. Designed by Parker.
(*Brown & Sharpe*)

30. This invention produced quite a patent controversy. Hendey Machine Company had an application for a patent for a constant speed drive for a lathe, No. 691,963 of January 28, 1902 (application, November 3, 1900). There was some degree of prior use in O. Mergenthaler, No. 636,914 of November 14, 1899. Parker filed application February 9, 1904, issued May 28, 1907 as No. 855,068. Cincinnati Milling Machine Company had used this feature and claimed protection by prior art and slight change of design. Kearney & Trecker changed design. Le Blond showed a modification in their application of November 28, 1904, issued May 2, 1905 as No. 788,658, and Cincinnati Milling Machine Company had A. L. De Leeuw's patent No. 980,614 of January 3, 1911. It was all worked out with outstanding good will on all sides.

31. Patent J. Parker, No. 1,032,698 of July 16, 1912.

32. Patent L. Thiel, No. 914,527 of March 9, 1909.

33. Patent W. P. Norton, No. 691,963 of January 28, 1902. Also J. Parker, No. 1,170,097 of February 1, 1916.

setting the cutter in relation to the work,[31] a safety to prevent gears being shifted while connected to the prime mover,[32] a spindle reverse,[33] friction intake for drive,[34] clutch drive for the spindle nose.[35] More important was the introduction of a satisfactory gear arrangement for the spindle drive. This is shown in various Cincinnati Milling Machine Company patents, the crucial one of which would seem to be R. T. Hazelton et al. March 5, 1918, No. 1,258,614. It was adopted by Brown & Sharpe under license in January 1924.[36]

The Brown & Sharpe machine of 1901 became the prototype of the Constant Speed Milling Machine of the present day. Taken together with positive connections to the feed, speeds in geometrical progression, and devices permitting convenient choice in feed speeds either independent of or dependent on the spindle speed, it has revolutionized milling machine design, and made possible Constant Speed Motor Drives.

Motor Drive

About the turn of the century more and more tool engineers were thinking of the advantages to be gained if the then common method of overhead pulleys driven by a large single prime mover could be replaced by individual drive of each machine tool by an electric motor. This would seem at first a simple problem, but it involved the redesign of the tools and design of suitable electric motors. The central problem proved to be the difficulty of designing an electric motor with adequate power at varying speeds. The story of this problem is a most interesting one.

The ideal solution was to have a variable speed motor working directly on the spindle of the machine tool, thus

34. Used on Cincinnati millers in 1904. See *Iron Age,* January, 1904, p. 15; *American Machinist,* 1903, p. 1843; Horner, *op. cit.,* p. 39.

35. Patent Kearney & Trecker, No. 1,053,296 of February 18, 1913. Another form had been used on Bement & Niles Milling Machine of 1900 and adopted by Brown & Sharpe in 1916. Cincinnati Milling Machine Company had used their form as early as 1914. Ingersoll claimed that they originated the principle, but no evidence has been found for this.

36. This patent is perhaps anticipated by the Albert Herbert milling machine shown in *Iron Age* for January 2, 1913, pp. 98-100. Herbert also included a clutch drive for the spindle nose.

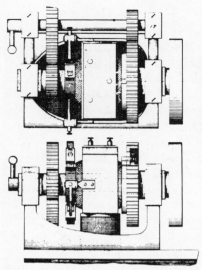

FIG. 29. MOTOR-DRIVEN LATHE,
J. J. SPRAGUE, 1890.
(*U. S. Patent*)

eliminating the problem of complex gearing. This was attempted for the lathe by Joseph J. Sprague in his patent No.
437,259 of July 19, 1890 (Fig. 29). A number of other
inventors' efforts are shown in the patent files. The problem
proved to be more complex than this.

In August of 1899 Brown & Sharpe asked the General
Electric Company for detailed information on the application of variable speed motors to milling machines. General
Electric replied that they hoped to submit a practical scheme
in a few days. In December Brown & Sharpe asked for the
long delayed plans, but evidently nothing further came of
it.[37] Brown & Sharpe went ahead on their own. By January
1901 they had applied a General Electric four-speed direct
current motor to one of their No. 5 Plain Milling Machines.
Fig. 30 indicates the resulting ungainly design. By the end
of September 1904 they had made a little progress. Fig. 31
shows one of their No. 3 Universal Milling Machines at the
Brooklyn Navy Yard using a 4 H. P. General Electric motor
on a 15 H. P. frame, speeds 375-1400 rpm, 110 volts D. C.
While the design improved somewhat, these experiments[38]

37. See Brown & Sharpe files.
38. Cincinnati Milling Machine Company actually put on the market in 1903
a form of their large No. 5 cone driven machine with a 2:1 variable speed
motor using a combination of back gears and silent chain drive to get a
wide range of speeds. See *American Machinist* 1903, p. 1843.

70

FIG. 30. AN EARLY ATTEMPT TO MOTORIZE THE MILLING MA-CHINE, 1901. (*Brown & Sharpe*)

FIG. 31. PROGRESS IN MOTORIZING THE MILLING MACHINE, 1904. (*Brown & Sharpe*)

FIG. 32. CINCINNATI MOTOR-DRIVEN MILLING MACHINE OF 1903.
With friction clutch and all-gear drive of the spindle. (*Cincinnati*)

FIG. 33. SUCCESSFUL CONSTANT SPEED ELECTRIC MOTOR DRIVE, 1919. (*Brown & Sharpe*)

served only to show the excessive size of the motor required, the greater cost of the motor, and the greater power consumption, especially at slow speeds and coarse feeds. The variable speed electric motor was not the answer.

The answer was, of course, to use a constant speed electric motor, of adequate power, to run a constant speed drive machine. The Cincinnati Milling Machine Company had at the turn of the century attacked the problem of electric motor drive, using constant speed motors acting through a friction clutch and an all-geared drive of the spindle. By 1903 they were offering the machine shown in Fig. 32 to the trade.[39] Various locations of the motor were tried — on top of the column or bolted to the frame — before the motor was finally located on a base cast integral with the base of the machine as standard.[40] From this it was but a short step to put the motor in the base. This was done for some machine tools as early as 1902, but the first use of this feature in a knee-type milling machine was made by Brown & Sharpe in 1919 (Fig. 33). With this advance the spindle design and the method of powering it reached essentially their modern form.

Feed Mechanisms and Their Control

Some of the limitations of milling machine feed designs had been realized in the 1880's. As early as 1884 Fred J. Miller raised the issue in an article in the *American Machinist*.[41] He pointed out the disadvantages of having the feed dependent on the spindle speed. He summed them up:

"This leads me to humbly suggest that it would be more in accordance with the eternal fitness of things if the ratio between extremes of speed bore some relation to the ratio between the necessary extremes in sizes of cutters."

Miller went on to suggest a system of feed pulleys in such a way as to approach his ideal more nearly. This method was later adopted by some milling machine manufacturers.

Miller's principle was developed more scientifically and systematically by the use of transposing pulleys to give

39. *American Machinist,* 1903, p. 1843, and *Iron Age,* January 7, 1904, p. 13.
40. *American Machinist,* 1904, p. 1579.
41. *American Machinist,* September 20, 1884, p. 4.

geometric progression of feeds, when L. D. Burlingame and J. W. Boynton of Brown & Sharpe worked out the necessary formulas.[42] These principles were incorporated in Brown & Sharpe milling machines as early as 1888. Feeds using either gears or belts in geometric progression were patented by Carl G. Barth in 1895.[43] Brown & Sharpe adopted this method;[44] later John Parker was issued a patent for this feature.[45]

The Cincinnati Milling Machine Company was awarded a gold medal at the Paris Exposition of 1900 for a new design of milling machine (Fig. 34).[46] This was the first milling machine with all-gear positive-drive feed mechanisms. Brown & Sharpe had developed John Parker's feed[47] but soon abandoned it for the improved type. Central feed was the work of L. Cosgrove of Pedrick & Ayer.[48]

42. The formulas were given by C. C. Stutz in *Machinery*, May, 1899, pp. 261-266.

43. Patent No. 547,474 of October 5, 1895 (application, January 20, 1894).

44. *American Machinist*, October 22, 1903, pp. 1481-83, and September 26, 1907, pp. 429-432.

45. Patent No. 855,068 of May 28, 1907.

46. Patent F. Holz, No. 658,777 of October 2, 1900.

47. Patent No. 682,227 of September 10, 1901. Also see his patent No. 754,339 of March 8, 1904.

48. Patent No. 282,704 of August 7, 1883.

Fig. 34. Cincinnati All-Geared Drive Milling Machine of 1906. (*Cincinnati*)

These developments, of course, provided the basis for geared feeds whether independent of or dependent on spindle speeds. But all this was essentially only a makeshift solution.

The theoretical considerations of feed speeds were again taken up in an editorial in the *American Machinist*.[49] After comparison of the problem in the lathes and in milling machines the editor concludes:

". . . feed motion should be derived from some part of the machine having a uniform rate of rotation, independent of spindle rate of rotation."

This was what Mergenthaler did in part in 1898 and what Parker was the first to do completely for the milling machine in 1900. These men were thinking in terms of a belt and cone drive; it was the coming of individual motor drives that made the problem more evident and led to the solution in terms of a constant speed drive with feeds independent of spindle speeds.

The Gabriel milling machine patent application of 1899 had already utilized the principle of feeds independent of spindle speeds, but the really crucial invention for proper feed control on the milling machine was John Parker's memorandum of December 14, 1900[50] as applied to Brown & Sharpe machines September 1901.[51] E. J. McClellan of the Garvin Machine Company designed[52] a feed either dependent on or independent of spindle speeds. This was used on Brown & Sharpe No. 4 Universal Milling Machine in June 1907, but seems to have been dropped. The Cincinnati line of high power milling machines introduced in 1907 and

49. "Milling Machine Feeds," *American Machinist*, July 26, 1894, p. 8.

50. See above p. 66.

51. See Fig. 28 and detailed description in *American Machinist*, October 22, 1903, pp. 1481-83.

52. Patent No. 800,470 of September 26, 1905.

1908 had independent feed and spindle drives (Fig. 22) and were available, because of their unit construction, as pulley and cone drive, variable speed motor drive, or constant speed motor drive. The feed drive was available in inches per minute or in inches per spindle revolution. With this design the feed rate was set to meet production requirements and cutter capabilities in terms of chip or feed per tooth (as suggested by Holz many years earlier), and the speed was selected on the ability of the cutter to stand the effects of the temperature of the cut.[53]

Separate feed control led to a large number of signifi-cant technical advances and to many convenience features: visual reading,[54] single lever control for shifting gears,[55] directional lever for each feed,[56] independent clutches for each feed,[57] safety interlock for cross and vertical feeds to prevent simultaneous engagement,[58] table feed to avoid torsion by bringing the drive near the center instead of at the end,[59] control of power feed from the front,[60] control

53. *American Machinist*, 1908, pp. 401-410.

54. See Fred Holz patent No. 554,422 of February 11, 1896. Garvin Machine Company's Patent, E. J. McClellan, No. 641,219 of January 9, 1900. R. F. Scott et al., No. 798,462 of August 29, 1905.

55. Alfred Herbert et al., No. 742,025 of October 20, 1903. Cincinnati Milling Machine Co. Patents, S. Einstein, No. 1,120,650 of December 8, 1914. R. T. Hazelton et al., No. 1,125,686 of January 19, 1915, and R. T. Hazelton, No. 1,125,905 of September 9, 1919.

56. Patented by R. T. Hazelton, No. 1,315,722 of January 19, 1915. A Cincinnati Milling Machine Co. feature described in *American Machinist*, September 17, 1908, pp. 401-410.

57. Another Cincinnati Milling Machine Co. feature, patent R. T. Hazelton, No. 1,125,905 of January 19, 1915.

58. Patent B. P. Graves, No. 1,286,292 of December 3, 1918.

59. Patent J. Parker, No. 1,295,583 of February 25, 1919.

60. A Cincinnati Milling Machine Co. feature having the feed mechanism located in the saddle. Patents: S. Einstein, No. 1,120,650 of December 8, 1914, and A. L. De Leeuw, No. 1,130,685 of March 2, 1915. This feature also used by Garvin Machine Co. Patent: E. J. McClellan, No. 502,131 of July 25, 1893.

from either front or rear,[61] single clutch connected to operate all feeds.[62] There were also a number of features to provide slow, fast, reverse and quick return of the table.[63]

Spiral Head and Foot Stock

As we have already seen, various indexing heads had been developed by the French clockmakers of the 18th century. Nasmyth had made the first and much wider application to the milling machine, and Frederick W. Howe had fitted a very clumsy form of indexing head to his Robbins & Lawrence "universal" miller of 1850. Here again Joseph R. Brown had made the crucial invention in his universal milling machine of 1861. This rather specialized attachment for the milling machine has not received as much attention from inventors as some of the more basic elements, especially after 1900. A device to provide rigid support when the spiral head is set at an angle was patented by C. E. Lipe.[64] Independent indexing received attention from V. H. Ernst[65] and C. H. Phillips.[66] Fred Holtz invented in 1890 the universal dividing head which has been improved by the Cincinnati Milling Machine Company by adding the long and short lead attachment, the wide range divider, and the

61. Le Blond had this feature, patent No. 932,791 of August 31, 1909. Also patent of N. Leerberg, No. 1,480,910 of January 15, 1924 provides for control of both feed and spindle speed change mechanisms.

62. A Kempsmith feature. Patents No. 480,198 of August 2, 1892 and No. 538,260 of April 30, 1895. Also in Cincinnati Milling Machine Co., A. L. De Leeuw, No. 961,405 of June 14, 1910 and A. L. De Leeuw, No. 973,766 of October 25, 1910.

63. Patents: S. L. Worsley, No. 497,850 of May 23, 1893. Oscar J. Beale, No. 631,923 of August 29, 1899. J. Parker, No. 642,711 of February 6, 1900. S. Einstein, No. 1,092,097 of March 31, 1914. J. Parker, No. 1,196,882 and No. 1,196,883 of September 5, 1916. R. T. Hazelton, No. 1,390,706 of September 13, 1921.

64. Patent No. 292,927 of February 5, 1884.

65. Patent No. 341,437 of May 4, 1886.

66. Patent No. 343,846 of June 15, 1886.

FIG. 35. CINCINNATI MILLING MA-
CHINE DIVIDING HEAD OF 1901.
(*Cincinnati*)

high number index plates[67] (Fig. 35). The principal improvement in this feature was the differential indexing of
A. L. De Leeuw.[68] He invented this without thought of its
use on a milling machine. That application was conceived
by L. D. Burlingame of Brown & Sharpe, who secured the
patent.[69] Later it was discovered that the broad features
had been anticipated in an old patent of 1856 by William
H. Brown.[70] John Parker added a fine auxiliary adjustment
for indexing.[71] J. W. Boynton invented the now widely used
elevating foot stock.[72] Fred Holz of the Cincinnati Milling
Machine Company invented the dividing head footstock
with two center points and vertical and horizontal adjustments to accommodate taper work, as well as heavy work.
He also invented a drive for cutting spirals obtained by
driving the dividing head from the table lead screw through
change gears.[73]

67. See Fred Holz patent No. 432,621 of July 22, 1890, and also their
patents No. 1,865,552 of July 5, 1932, No. 1,936,257 of November 21, 1933,
No. 2,002,816 of May 28, 1935, and No. 2,101,544 of December 7, 1937.

68. Patent No. 686,266 of November 12, 1901.

69. This was before A. L. De Leeuw's long and fruitful association with the
Cincinnati Milling Machine Co.

70. *American Machinist*, 1907, p. 859. Patent No. 14,082 of June 15, 1856.

71. Patent No. 1,295,363 of February 25, 1919.

72. Patent No. 491,521 of February 14, 1893. But see A. H. Brainard's
patent No. 110,951 of January 17, 1871.

73. F. Holz patent No. 432,621 of July 22, 1890. Compare this device with
that on Joseph R. Brown's universal miller of 1861.

Hand Adjustment of Table

In 1881-1882 the Cincinnati Milling Machine Company first introduced the placing of crank or hand wheels at an angle so as to clear each other.[74] This machine was also the first centralized control milling machine (Fig. 36). By having the spindle rotating anti-clockwise this miller could use standard drills, boring tools, reamers, etc., designed for drill presses and lathes. This naturally required placing the indexing head on the right hand side of the table (Fig. 35). The operator thus logically stood on the left hand side of the knee where he could conveniently operate from one point the table controls, the knee controls, and the lever to the countershaft belt. With their swivel vise and the Holz and Mueller dividing head this machine was especially convenient for high accuracy in gear cutting.[75] In 1899 O. J. Beale invented a hand quick-return movement which

74. Patent F. Holz, No. 513,682 of January 30, 1894.
75. Sol Einstein's paper, pp. 3-4.

FIG. 36. CINCINNATI'S CENTRALIZED CONTROL MILLER, 1881.
(*Cincinnati*)

preserved the directional revolution by direct internal gearing.[76] Quick or slow traverse of the table by the same hand wheel was patented by J. Edgar of Becker-Brainard Milling Machine Company,[77] but seldom used after power quick return was generally adopted. Provision for the hand wheel to stand still while power traverse is operating was made in Brown & Sharpe machines in 1911-1912.

Oiling System

The first patent for a general oiling system of the bearings and gears of a milling machine was that of Kearney & Trecker.[78] De Leeuw designed an oiling system using gravity feed from a reservoir into which the oil was pumped.[79] Brown & Sharpe had designed a similar system used in October 1901.

A device which also provided for oiling the saddle and knee mechanisms was covered in patents to J. Goetz, of Kempsmith.[80] Similar features were used after 1925 by both Brown & Sharpe and Cincinnati Milling Machine Company.[81]

Cutters and Use of Coolant

We have seen the multiplication of milling cutters after 1865. It was not until the work of Fred Holz and A. L. De Leeuw at the Cincinnati Milling Machine Company that

76. Patent No. 631,923 of August 29, 1899.

77. Patent No. 937,057 of October 29, 1902.

78. Patent No. 995,256 of June 13, 1911 (application, February 17, 1906).

79. Patent No. 1,093,118 of April 14, 1914.

80. Patents No. 1,087,364 and No. 1,087,365 of February 17, 1914.

81. Cincinnati Milling Machine Company advertisements in *Machinery*, November, 1925.

FIG. 37. COMPARISON OF DE LEEUW DESIGN OF MILLING CUTTERS
WITH EARLIER FORMS.
In each example the De Leeuw cutter is shown on the right.
Note the much wider spacing of De Leeuw's teeth.
(*Cincinnati*)

any really systematic and adequate scientific study was made
of the stresses developed by these cutters, and designs based
upon these scientific results were brought out.[82]

De Leeuw's analysis had shown that the cutters of the
time were not as strong as the machines that were driving
them and therefore gave out long before the maximum
power of the machine was reached. On this basis Cincinnati
Milling Machine Company designed a new face mill, later
marketed by Union Twist Drill Company, which increased
the metal removal per horsepower by 50%. Further experiments on a larger scale were carried out by A. L. De Leeuw
at Cincinnati Milling Machine Company [83] which led to the
design of wide-spaced cutters as more durable and more
efficient in removing metal (Fig. 37). The work was con-

82. *American Machinist,* 1904, pp. 404, 882 and 1149. John Parker at
Brown & Sharpe had made somewhat less extensive tests (idem). P. V.
Vernon was also working on this problem. (*Engineer,* May 31, 1907, pp.
542-544.) See also the work of Lewis & Taylor in *Trans. Am. Soc. Mech.
Eng.,* 1908, p. 869.
83. *Trans. Am. Soc. Mech. Eng.,* 1911, p. 245.

tinued in studies of rake angles, steep spirals, and staggered teeth. To the genius of A. L. De Leeuw and the farsighted policy of the Cincinnati Milling Machine Company must go the credit for bringing scientific methods to bear on the milling cutter, as Taylor and White had done for single-point tools.

Coolant for milling cutters had been used by Nasmyth. The considerable heat locally generated by multiple cutters made this necessary very early. The usual method was one still employed — simply a can with an adjustable pipe to drip the coolant directly on the cutter. With higher production rates and heavier cuts a more elaborate and continuous system became necessary. The first patent using a pump was that of W. Krutzsch[84] adopted by Brown & Sharpe about 1893. The idea of using the base to form the coolant tank was broadly implied in Krutzsch's patent, but the specific patents are those of A. L. De Leeuw (Cincinnati Milling Machine Company),[85] F. A. Parsons (Kempsmith Milling Machine Company),[86] and W. F. Groene (R. K. Le Blond Machine Tool Company).[87] By 1918 nearly all milling machine manufacturers had this feature.

This represents the development of the milling machine, especially of the knee type down to about 1926. By 1908 scientific studies of its performance had been begun by A. L. De Leeuw of Cincinnati Milling Machine Company,[88] and the further development of this basic type of milling machine had by 1926 passed from the hands of the inventor into those of the tool engineer.

84. Patent No. 166,704 of August 17, 1875.

85. Patent No. 1,093,118 of April 14, 1914.

86. Patent No. 1,270,862 of July 2, 1918.

87. Patent No. 1,316,230 of September 16, 1919.

88. *Trans. Am. Soc. Mech. Eng.*, 1908, p. 837. It was not until 1956 that a milling machine departing from traditional major components and based on calculation from basic mechanical principles was marketed by Saviem in France.

V Evolution of New Types —

Vertical Spindle, Specialized and Automatic

VERTICAL SPINDLE

SPECIALIZED TYPES

AUTOMATIC MILLING MACHINES

FLUID DRIVE

TRACER AND ELECTRONIC CONTROLS

EVOLUTION OF NEW TYPES

We have thus far neglected a number of types of milling machines of prime importance in modern machine shop work, in order to bring out the fundamental lines of development. These types also bring us to a new era in the growth of the milling machine, in that British and continental designers introduced after 1900 important and original contributions — especially to the vertical spindle machines. For automatic milling machines the early work was done by smaller independent firms and then taken up by the Cincinnati Milling Machine Company, who became the leaders in innovation in both mechanical and hydraulic automatic controls. This phase also includes the beginnings of electronic controls, principally for the die-sinker type, and in this connection Pratt & Whitney again comes to the fore.

Vertical Spindle

The first clear record of a vertical spindle milling machine is to be found in the drawings of W. B. Bement's patent referred to above.[1] The drawings are incidental to Bement's claim for use of the interior of the stand for storage of tools, etc. Bement refers to a vertical milling machine in terms which clearly indicate that it was no new thing, for he shows a quite detailed drawing of a well developed machine (Fig. 38) with a plano-miller type of support for a spindle mounted on slides to give vertical or transverse feed by a wheel operating a rack-and-pinion. Power is provided for transverse feed, but apparently not for vertical feed. Both the spindle and the spindle slide have their weight counterbalanced. The table is supported on the base and a fixed knee and has only hand feed in traverse and cross feed, very much resembling the table and support of the Bement & Dougherty plain milling machine of this period.

James Watson's vertical milling machine of 1870, while especially designed for cutting key ways, was recognized

1. Patent No. 35,433 of June 3, 1862.

84

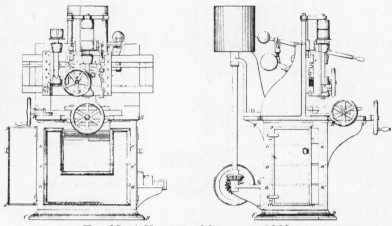

FIG. 38. A VERTICAL MILLER OF 1862.
(*U. S. Patent*)

by the inventor as "adapted to a great variety of work."[2] It is the earliest machine to have the general appearance of the vertical spindle milling machine[3] — with a spindle capable of vertical motion over a table movable in traverse only, the spindle driven by bevel gearing from a belt cone. Watson provided for the whole spindle assembly to slide vertically and the power drive to remain in mesh with the gear on the cone shaft by means of an ingenious combination of gears and links. This machine left much to be desired, but it was a good first attempt.

Somewhat later in England, George Richards obtained a patent[4] for a vertical miller using a planer type head but having a swiveling table, power feed for traverse and cross feed, a friction wheel drive to give reverse, and a worm wheel drive of the spindle.

Multiple spindles in a turret appeared in a patent of E. Rivett.[5] A number of continental designers tried similar

2. Patent No. 98,821 of January 11, 1870.
3. But see the 1867 machine of J. E. Reinecker in Germany, *American Machinist*, 1913, p. 890.
4. British patent No. 12,076 of August 2, 1890.
5. Patent No. 487,160 of November 29, 1892.

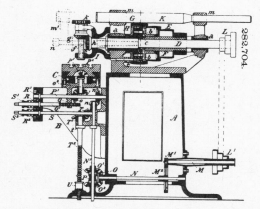

FIG. 39. COSGROVE'S
VERTICAL MILLING
MACHINE OF 1883.
(*U. S. Patent*)

turrets as well as many attempts to combine in one machine horizontal and vertical spindles.[6]

A significant step forward was taken in 1883 by L. Cosgrove with his vertical miller.[7] He provided for vertical, transverse, and longitudinal feed through a knee-and-column support of the table, and for swiveling of the spindle from vertical to the horizontal position or any angle in between (Fig. 39). This was a well-designed and ingenious machine.

Two years later Joseph Saget, of France, took out a British patent[8] on a vertical miller having a knee and column, vertical adjustment of the table, a spindle head which could swivel in both planes and having a table which could also swivel.

Many of these problems of the vertical milling machine had already been solved for the drill press, and for the early profiling and die-sinking machines,[9] but the solutions were

6. See A. Vernet's French patent No. 374,383 of June 11, 1907 which shows a turret head set at an angle to give both horizontal and vertical positions for the spindle.

7. Patent No. 282,704 of August 7, 1883.

8. British patent No. 6702 of June 2, 1885. See the description of this machine in P. Richards, *Traité des machines outils,* Paris, 1895, pp. 16 and 151.

9. See examples of Pratt & Whitney machines of 1876 in Joseph M. Wilson, *Masterpieces of the Centennial Exhibition 1876,* Philadelphia, n.d., Vol. III, p. 304.

only adapted fully to the milling machine by William W. Hulse [10] who modified the vertical slide of the spindle drill press for the vertical miller, without any vertical feed of the table. He also provided additional support for the cutter end of the spindle when profiling.

Since the vertical miller had been used mostly with end-mill type cutters it was soon found necessary to go to much higher spindle speeds. J. Becker attempted to get higher speeds by improved bearings,[11] and G. B. Beale provided for lubricating these cutters at high speeds by a small pump forcing the lubricant fluid through a tube inside the spindle.[12]

In 1906 two important steps were taken. C. R. Gabriel of Brown & Sharpe invented gearing to provide slow or rapid power vertical feed of the spindle.[13] And in England A. Herbert and P. V. Vernon devised gearing to give various speeds for power vertical feed of the spindle.[14]

In 1910 A. L. De Leeuw applied central drive to the spindle of the vertical miller.[15] In 1888 Brown & Sharpe had provided a vertical attachment for their plain miller; in 1911 G. D. Sundstrand patented a similar attachment for their universal miller.[16]

By 1906, then, various types of production vertical millers were in use (Fig 40), with fixed or swiveling heads, fixed or adjustable tables, having power feed in two directions and often vertically. The features described in the previous section for horizontal spindle machines were also rapidly applied to vertical millers to provide a most useful

10. British patent No. 2780 of February 11, 1893.

11. Patent No. 489,282 of January 3, 1893.

12. Patent No. 684,667 of October 15, 1901.

13. Patent No. 809,915 of January 9, 1906.

14. British patent No. 6491 of December 6, 1906, and French patent No. 370,003 of January 26, 1907.

15. Patent No. 974,036 of October 25, 1910.

16. Brown & Sharpe Catalogue 1888, p. 53. Sundstrand's patent No. 1,008,753 of November 14, 1911.

FIG. 40. A. HERBERT'S VERTICAL SPINDLE MILLER, 1906.
(*Parr*)

and convenient machine tool. The vertical miller gave convenience in handling heavy castings and reduced deformation due to casting weight. It was able to do the face and both edges without resetting the work. It was also easily adapted to profile, contour, and die-sinking types.

Perhaps the most important development of the vertical milling machine was the jig borer, for it was this which made possible the wide use of precision jigs. It was the use of such jigs which permitted the use of semi-skilled labor in the production of precision parts.[17]

17. Their development will be considered in a later monograph, *History of Jigs, Fixtures, Arbors and Chucks.*

Brown & Sharpe had already applied micrometer scales and verniers to milling machines when in 1903 a vertical spindle miller was used for jig boring.[18] It was not until 1910, however, that Le Blond brought out a vertical miller especially designed and equipped for jig boring.[19]

Specialized Types

As the milling machine came to have wider use after the turn of the century, it was put to doing heavier work and adapted to specialized work. The advantages of milling over planing, even for large pieces such as locomotive parts, led to the development of the plano-millers, of both horizontal and vertical spindle types.[20] Multiple spindle millers, both horizontal and vertical, proved of advantage in doing complex milling. In 1913 the Cincinnati Milling Machine Company brought out for Ford a special machine for milling the connections on cylinder heads of automobile engines (Fig. 41). This had a semi-automatic standard head, intermittent feed, and quick traverse. The clamping and release of the work was automatic through a stationary cam. This machine is representative of a number of specialized milling machines designed to meet the high production rates demanded by the automotive industry. Fig. 42 illustrates the modern development of specialized, fully automatic milling machines, in this case a tracer-controlled machine for milling six turbine buckets at one time.

Millers were built for milling threads and flutes. Especially significant were millers designed only for gear cutting.[21] Several manufacturers brought out very extensive lines of attachments for their milling machines to adapt them to shaping, slotting, and many other forms of work.

18. *American Machinist,* 1903, p. 348. Brown & Sharpe Catalogue for 1903.
19. *Machinery,* February 1910, p. 493.
20. First patent J. E. Sweet, No. 565,642 of August 11, 1896.
21. This development is taken up in detail in R. S. Woodbury, *History of the Gear-Cutting Machine,* The Technology Press, Cambridge, Mass., 1958.

Fig. 41. Special Rotary Miller of 1913,
for Milling Ford Cylinder Heads.
(*Cincinnati*)

Fig. 42. Modern Specialized Tracer-Controlled Milling Machine.
For contour milling six turbine buckets simultaneously.
(*Cincinnati*)

In 1937 Brown & Sharpe brought out their "Omni-versal" milling machine.[22] At first many manufacturers believed this to be of only limited application, but experience in World War II showed it to be a most useful machine tool. It was widely copied in England, France, Germany, and Italy.

A most important form of specialized milling machine of the vertical spindle type is the various profilers and die-sinkers. J. Price developed one specially for internal profiling of cams,[23] and a type of more general application to both profiling and die-sinking was invented by F. D. Van Dorman.[24] With H. M. Albee's pressure point die-sinker[25] we have all the essential elements of the die-sinker until we get automatic and electronic controls.

Automatic Milling Machines

Up to about 1910 the knee-and-column type of milling machine, as we have seen it develop, and the improved bed, or Lincoln type, milling machine had been adequate to meet production demands. However, as industry, especially the automotive industry, began to make increased demands on all machine tools for higher production rates, the grinding machine, the gear-cutter, the milling machine, and many other machine tools were increasingly designed for automatic action to give higher production rates at lower costs. The knee-and-column type miller was too complex to be adapted to many manufacturing purposes and tended to be relegated to tool room work and to small lot production. The simplicity of the bed type miller led to its becoming the basic type for automatic milling machines.

The development of automatic controls — mechanical, hydraulic, electric, and electronic—has made possible milling

22. Patent A. F. Bennett, No. 2,094,484 of September 28, 1937.
23. Patent No. 564,800 of July 28, 1896.
24. Patent No. 659,461 of October 9, 1900.
25. Patent No. 734,792 of July 28, 1903.

machines of far greater size and much wider application in production. But this technical advance was made possible by a series of technical innovations too specialized to be mentioned other than briefly to indicate the highlights.

The early work to make the milling machine automatic begins with E. F. Latham's automatic reverse and quick return mechanism using a worm device.[26] O. Schonauer, of Austria, attempted the same results by use of a swinging shaft, but although a patent was granted[27] there is some doubt that the device would actually work. C. Hakes and F. P. Carter tried to solve the problem by the use of a chain drive.[28]

The first really significant step was taken by John Edgar[29] of Becker-Brainard who invented a locking and releasing device on the drive shaft, which ensured proper meshing of the gears. In 1908 rapid advance by hand to the desired point for shift to automatic feed was provided by William H. Stedman, through automatic yield to too high stresses.[30]

The crucial invention for automatic mechanical control was, however, that of E. Stuck, who provided fully automatic fast feed between cuts, slow cutting feeds, and quick return.[31] Other men simplified Stuck's tripping mechanism to use dogs similar to those of Stedman.[32]

Sol Einstein's device to add automatic feed to existing milling machines[33] and his centralized automatic control[34]

26. Patent No. 260,760 of July 11, 1882.
27. U. S. Patent No. 681,584 of August 27, 1901.
28. Patent No. 731,678 of June 23, 1903.
29. Patent No. 790,039 of May 16, 1905 (application October 29, 1902).
30. Patent No. 893,205 of July 14, 1908.
31. Patent No. 956,444 of April 26, 1910.
32. Patent H. F. Kelleman, No. 957,562 of May 10, 1910. British patent Fred Coxon, No. 15,639 of July 3, 1913. British patent Vincent Gartside, No. 17,749 of May 21, 1914.
33. Patent No. 1,092,479 of April 7, 1914.
34. Patent No. 1,124,117 of January 5, 1915.

FIG. 43. CINCINNATI'S "HIGH POWER" MILLING MACHINE OF 1917.
Note the massive rigidity of this machine.
(*Cincinnati*)

herald in 1910 the entrance of Cincinnati Milling Machine Company into the field of automatic control of milling machines, in which they were to take the lead. A long series of improvements in mechanical means of automatic control came in a flood over the next few years in the work of Einstein, Hazelton, De Leeuw and others, far too many to warrant even listing their patent numbers. A representative production example of the knee-and-column type is Cincinnati's No. 5 High Power Milling Machine (Fig. 43). The form and characteristics of the automatic bed type of milling machine (now commonly referred to as a "manufacturing milling machine") were set by the Cincinnati Milling Machine Company's automatic millers of 1913 (Fig. 44), based upon the work of De Leeuw.[35] By 1916 machines of this

35. See De Leeuw's patents No. 1,130,685 of March 2, 1915 and No. 1,132,534 of March 16, 1915.

FIG. 44. CINCINNATI'S MANUFACTURING MILLER OF 1913. Note that this machine has the Lincoln miller as an ancestor. (*Cincinnati*)

type were on the market in plain and duplex models having completely automatic operation of the table cycle from start with rapid advance, feed, rapid reversal and stop, and automatic spindle stop. Of course they rapidly replaced the Lincoln type millers, which were still being made.

Fluid Drive

The first attempt at fluid drive was that of J. D. Potter,[36] a clumsy machine but an outstanding first attempt. The Cincinnati Milling Machine Company took out patents for the hydraulic drive of H. Ernst and L. F. Nenninger.[37] This was followed rapidly by the work of Walter D. Archea,[38] Millard Romaine and Erwin G. Roehm,[39] and Mario E. Martellotti [40] and B. Sassen,[41] all of the Cincinnati Milling Machine Company. Work on this type of machine was then taken up by Sundstrand, Barnes, Fletcher, Ingersoll, and Kearney & Trecker.

In 1927 the Cincinnati Milling Machine Company produced the first standard milling machines to utilize hydraulic control and power drive for the feed of a milling machine table (Fig. 23). These bed type machines had separate feed and speed drives and infinitely variable table feed.[42] Hy-

36. Patent No. 1,829,943 of November 3, 1931 but note that date of application was December 8, 1921!

37. U. S. Patent No. 2,028,766 of January 28, 1936 (application November 17, 1927!). Swedish patent No. 69,207 of November 16, 1928. British patent No. 300,652 of October 10, 1929. Described in *Machinery*, November, 1929, pp. 240-241.

38: Patents No. 1,961,123 and No. 1,961,124 both of June 5, 1934.

39. Patent No. 1,972,818 of September 4, 1934.

40. Patent No. 1,978,350 of October 23, 1934.

41. Patents No. 2,044,020 of June 16, 1935 and No. 2,070,811 of February 16, 1937.

42. Patent Ernst & Nenninger, No. 1,835,976 of December 8, 1931 (application, September 15, 1927).

draulically controlled machines of this kind had many characteristics especially valuable for high production work:

a) Variable feed rate by means of cam control of the hydraulic feed mechanism, to maintain a maximum constant power through a cut of varying width or depth, resulting in a gain in time required to mill each piece.

b) Rise and fall of the spindle carrier by means of a cam follower, to machine contours or to step over obstructions between surfaces to be milled.

c) Positive stop and delay trip unit, to permit milling accurately to depth and to finish a cut without leaving tooth marks.

Increased production rates on these machines required special design for handling chips and coolant. Because these machines were designed on the principle of unit construction, a number of standard and semi-standard units could be easily assembled in a wide variety of combinations to provide the machine most suitable for a given production job.

The techniques developed for these millers were successfully applied by the Cincinnati Milling Machine Company to a fully automatic die-sinking machine in 1932 and to their vertical milling machines with depth control in 1935 (Fig. 45). These machines permitted production milling of a variety of parts which, because of their special problems could not be otherwise conveniently milled. When tracer control was added, these machines had a flexibility which made them easily tooled to produce unusual milled contours.

The production capabilities of automatic controls, both mechanical and hydraulic, created a need for a backlash eliminator to meet the requirements of certain types of milling jobs, such as turbine blades. When these were milled conventionally, marks were left on the surface which remained even after polishing; when climb milled no such marks were left, and polishing gave a fine smooth surface. The backlash eliminator also made it possible to mill parts at either end of the table and so increase production. Fix-

FIG. 45. CINCINNATI'S HYDRO-TEL OF 1936, HYDRAULICALLY
CONTROLLED VERTICAL MILLING MACHINE.
Note the provision for coolant and chip handling.
(*Cincinnati*)

tures were simplified, and climb milling permitted holding work not otherwise suitable for milling operations.

Brown & Sharpe used the design of De Vlieg[43] as improved by Graves & Bennett[44]. Cincinnati used the somewhat different approach of Fred Holz[45] as subsequently modified and improved by their engineers.

Tracer and Electronic Controls

Although an automatic tool resembling a milling machine, for shaping wooden butts for rifles, had been produced as

43. Patent No. 2,002,991 of May 28, 1935. But see A. H. Brainard's patent No. 131,733 of October 1, 1872.
44. Patent No. 2,077,408 of April 20, 1937 (electric). Patent No. 2,124,852 of July 26, 1938 (hydraulic).
45. Patent Holz No. 513,683 of January 30, 1894.

97

early as 1818 by Thomas Blanchard at the Springfield Armory,[46] it had not been possible to do similar work in iron because the master cam wore out quickly under the high pressure required. In 1903 H. M. Albee had devised a mechanical pressure point die-sinker,[47] but attempts to find a satisfactory means of making it automatic failed. What was needed was electrical or hydraulic automatic control. The increased use of dies for forging, casting, and pressing after World War I demanded a faster and cheaper method of producing them than by using highly skilled workers on conventional die-sinking and milling machines.

In 1920 J. C. Shaw invented an electrical sensing device[48] which required only a very light contact with the master cam. Its movements were fed into a servomechanism controlling the various feeds. Shaw's principles were later applied by Pratt & Whitney to the Keller die-sinkers (Fig. 46). In 1927 J. W. Anderson had developed the all-hydraulic, tracer-controlled milling machine, and it was applied to Cincinnati Milling Machine Company's Die-Sinker (Fig. 47), Hydro-Tel Machine, and Profiler.[49] All these machines depend for their operation upon a model or master (sometimes hand-made of some relatively hard material) in contact with a tracer which translates its deflection

46. Patent, no number, of January 20, 1820. Patent model in the collection of U. S. National Museum, Catalogue No. 244,883. An original machine of 1822 is still preserved at the Springfield Armory.

47. Patent No. 734,792 of July 28, 1903.

48. Shaw's basic patents are: No. 1,506,454 of August 26, 1924 (application February 6, 1920); No. 1,668,518 of May 1, 1928 (application October 28, 1924); No. 1,683,581 of September 4, 1928 (application March 4, 1924); No. 1,717,326 of June 11, 1929 (application December 30, 1926); No. 2,007,899 of July 9, 1936 (application January 5, 1933). See also description in *Machinery*, October, 1925, pp. 159 and 160, and in *American Machinist*, September 19, 1925, pp. 489-492.

49. The basic patents on the tracer-controlled Hydro-Tel are: J. W. Anderson, No. 1,952,230 of March 27, 1934 (application August 1, 1927); No. 2,036,362 of April 7, 1936 (application September 20, 1932); No. 2,142,061 of December 27, 1938 (application October 8, 1934); No. 2,332,533 of October 26, 1943 (application September 2, 1941). See descriptions in *Machinery*, November 3, 1939, p. 213, and December 7, 1939, p. 241.

FIG. 46. A KELLER DIE-SINKER.
Note the size of this specialized milling machine.
(*Pratt & Whitney*)

FIG. 47. TRACER-CONTROLLED HYDRAULIC DIE-SINKER OF 1932.
(*Cincinnati*)

into commands to the servo system operating the slides. Pratt & Whitney recently developed their "Veltrace" machine [50] in which the tracer does not actually touch the model. This permits models which are very soft or fragile to be used again and again. All these devices depend, however, upon hand-made models.

Cincinnati Milling Machine Company has recently developed a line tracer Hydro-Tel which will trace directly from a drawing by using a cathode-ray light and phototube to translate the drawing into commands to a servo system (Fig. 48, page 102).

Probably the most significant advance in the milling machine in recent years is that developed for the U.S. Air Force by the Massachusetts Institute of Technology (Fig. 49). In this machine [51] a large Cincinnati Hydro-Tel Vertical Miller was adapted to electronic controls. The drawings for the part are programmed on a tape fed into an electronic control system which actuates the hydraulic controls of the miller in three dimensions. A production type of tape-controlled milling machine is shown in Fig. 50. The potentialities of this type of machine are as yet far from being fully exploited, but seem clearly to be tremendous, especially for repeated short run production.

Similar methods have been applied to other machine tools in recent years, and the milling machine has even been controlled by tapes programed by an electronic computer. It is significant that these advanced means of control have been first applied both experimentally and in production to the most flexible of all the machine tools — the one which, together with the grinding machine, seems clearly to hold the greatest promise for the future — the milling machine.

---

50. The basic patents on the "Veltrace" are those of P. J. Campbell, No. 2,677,310 and No. 2,677,311, both of May 4, 1954 (application December 13, 1948 and November 2, 1950 respectively).

51. *Numerically Controlled Milling Machine, Part 2.* (*Final Report to the U. S. Air Force on Construction and Initial Operation*), Massachusetts Institute of Technology — Servo-mechanisms Laboratory, May, 1953.

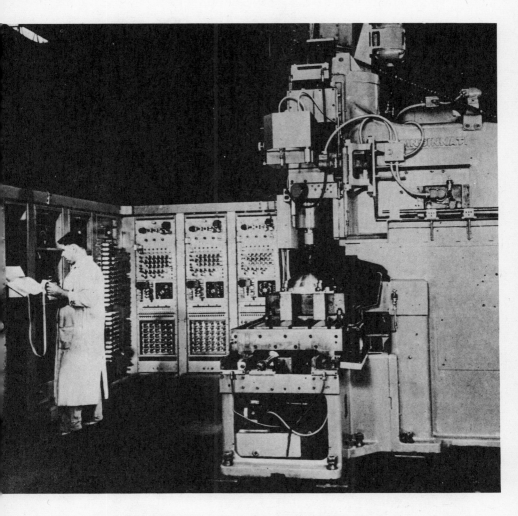

FIG. 49. THE M.I.T. TAPE-CONTROLLED MILLING MACHINE.
The milling machine of the future?
(*Massachusetts Institute of Technology*)

FIG. 50. A MODERN NUMERICALLY CONTROLLED SKIN MILL.
(*Cincinnati*)

FIG. 48. CINCINNATI'S LINE TRACER HYDRO-TEL MILLING MACHINE.
(*Cincinnati*)

BIBLIOGRAPHY

Books

ACADÉMIE ROYALE DES SCIENCES. *Machines et inventions approuvées par l'Académie Royale des Sciences,* Paris, 1735.

BERTHOUD, FERDINAND. *Essai sur l'horlogerie,* 3 vols., Paris, 1763 and 1786.

BESSON, JACQUES. *Theatrum instrumentorum et machinarum,* Lugduni, 1578.

BRAMAH, JOSEPH. *Dissertation on the Construction of Locks,* London, ca. 1815.

BROWN & SHARPE MFG. CO., *Treatise on Milling Machines,* Providence, R. I., 1893.

BUCHANAN, ROBERTSON. *Practical Essays on Mill Work and Other Machinery,* London, 1841.

BURLINGAME, LUTHER D. *History of Milling Machine Features,* unpublished typescript in files of Brown & Sharpe Mfg. Co., Providence, R. I.

BURLINGAME, LUTHER D. *Milling Machine Evolution,* unpublished typescript in files of Brown & Sharpe Mfg. Co., Providence, R. I.

CARDEN, GODFREY L. *Machine Tool Trade in Germany, France, Switzerland, Italy and United Kingdom,* Washington, GPO, 1909.

CONSERVATOIRE DES ARTS ET MÉTIERS. *Catalogue officiel des collections,* vol. 3, Paris, 1906.

DIDEROT, DENIS *Encyclopedie,* Paris, 1772.

EINSTEIN, SOL. *Forty Years of Milling Machine Development by the Cincinnati Milling Machine Company,* unpublished typescript in files of Cincinnati Milling Machine Co., June 23, 1923.

FITCH, CHARLES H. "Interchangeable Manufactures" in *Report on Manufactures of the U.S. Tenth Census of 1880,* Washington, GPO, 1883.

HICKS, JAMES E. *United States Ordnance,* Mt. Vernon, New York, 1940.

HORNER, JOSEPH. *Modern Milling Machines,* London, 1906.

MASSACHUSETTS INSTITUTE OF TECHNOLOGY. *Numerically Controlled Milling Machine, Part 2 (Final Report to the U.S. Air Force on Construction and Initial Operation),* Massachusetts Institute of Technology — Servomechanisms Laboratory, 1953.

NASMYTH, JAMES. *Autobiography,* (ed. Samuel Smiles), London, 1883.

PARR, ALFRED. *Machine Tools and Workshop Practice,* New York, 1905.

REES, ABRAHAM. *Cyclopedia or Universal Dictionary of Arts, Sciences and Literature,* Philadelphia, (1st Am. ed.), 1805-1825.

RICHARDS, P. *Traité des machines outils,* Paris, 1895.

ROBINSON, H. and ADAMS, W., eds. *Diary of Robert Hooke 1672-1680,* London, 1935.

ROE, JOSEPH W. *English and American Tool Builders,* New York, 1926.

SMILES, SAMUEL. *Industrial Biography,* Boston, 1864.

THIOUT, ANTOINE. *Traité de l'horlogerie méchanique et practique,* Paris, 1741.

THURSTON, ROBERT H. *Report on Machinery and Manufacturers, Vienna International Exhibition 1873,* Washington, GPO, 1875.

U. S. COMMISSIONERS. *Reports of the U.S. Commissioners to the Universal Exposition of 1889 at Paris,* vol. 3, Washington, 1891.

U. S. NATIONAL MUSEUM. *Catalogue,* Washington, GPO, 1939.

WILSON, JOSEPH M. *Masterpieces of the Centennial International Exhibition 1876,* Philadelphia, n.d.

WOODBURY, ROBERT S. *History of the Gear-Cutting Machine,* The Technology Press, Cambridge, Mass., 1958.

Journals

American Machinist
Engineer
Harper's Weekly
Iron Age
Iron Trade Review
Machinery (New York)
Practical Mechanics Journal (Glasgow)
Proceedings, Institution of Mechanical Engineers
Scientific American
Transactions, American Society of Mechanical Engineers
Vermont Journal, (Windsor, Vermont)

Other Sources

Patent Files: U.S.A., Great Britain and France. (All patent references are to U.S. patents unless otherwise indicated)

Industrial Files:

A wealth of information has been found in the files and sales records of Brown & Sharpe Mfg. Co., and in their catalogues for 1867, 1877, 1883, 1888 and 1903. The files of Cincinnati Milling Machine Company, Cincinnati, Ohio have also provided much valuable material.

INDEX